Tolley's
Tax Office Directory
2017

First edition

Edited by

Sylvia Courtnage
MA

Robin Farrow
MPhil

Members of the LexisNexis Group worldwide

United Kingdom	Reed Elsevier (UK) Limited trading as LexisNexis, 1–3 Strand, London WC2N 5JR
Australia	Reed International Books Australia Pty Ltd trading as LexisNexis, Chatswood, New South Wales
Austria	LexisNexis Verlag ARD Orac GmbH & Co KG, Vienna
Benelux	LexisNexis Benelux, Amsterdam
Canada	LexisNexis Canada, Markham, Ontario
China	LexisNexis China, Beijing and Shanghai
France	LexisNexis SA, Paris
Germany	LexisNexis GmbH, Dusseldorf
Hong Kong	LexisNexis Hong Kong, Hong Kong
India	LexisNexis India, New Delhi
Italy	Giuffrè Editore, Milan
Japan	LexisNexis Japan, Tokyo
Malaysia	Malayan Law Journal Sdn Bhd, Kuala Lumpur
New Zealand	LexisNexis NZ Ltd, Wellington
Singapore	LexisNexis Singapore, Singapore
South Africa	LexisNexis, Durban
USA	LexisNexis, Dayton, Ohio

© Reed Elsevier (UK) Ltd 2016
Published by LexisNexis

ISBN for this volume: 9780754552710

Printed and bound in Great Britain by Hobbs the Printers Ltd, Totton, Hampshire

Visit LexisNexis at www.lexisnexis.co.uk

The publishers wish to record their thanks to Her Majesty's Revenue and Customs and the predecessor Departments of Inland Revenue and Customs and Excise, without whose help this directory could not have been compiled. The information contained in this edition of Tolley's Tax Office Directory 2017 was current as at 1 October 2017.

Inevitably, some addresses (postal and email), telephone and fax numbers, and other additional information will change further. Details of any changes are welcomed by the publishers, and should be sent to the editors: Tax Office Directory, LexisNexis, Content Delivery Department, Tolley House, 30 Farringdon Street, London EC4A 4HH, England; email: robin.farrow@lexisnexis.co.uk; Internet: www.lexisnexis.co.uk.

Table of Contents

HM Revenue & Customs Office Structure

Organisational structure

The single department of HM Revenue & Customs (HMRC) amalgamated the Inland Revenue and HM Customs & Excise on 18 April 2005. HMRC is a non-ministerial department and as such, unlike most other Government departments, does not work under the day-to-day control of a minister. The Queen appoints Commissioners of HMRC who have responsibility for handling taxpayers' affairs impartially. The names of the Commissioners are published on the HMRC website (www.gov.uk/government/organisations/hm-revenue-customs/groups/hmrc-commissioners). Edward Troup is Executive Chair and First Permanent Secretary at HMRC and Jon Thompson is Chief Ex ecutive and First Permanent Secretary.

HMRC recently announced a restructure, so that from October 2016, the directorates in HMRC's four existing lines of business will be reorganised into three new groups:

- a new **customer strategy and tax design group**, which brings together customer strategy, tax policy, process design and tax assurance teams, led by Jim Harra;
- an expanded **customer service group**, which includes all of the big operational teams, led by Ruth Owen; and
- a **customer compliance group**, which will tackle non-compliance and enforcement for all customer groups, including large businesses, led by Jennie Granger.

The department will begin moving to the new model from 1 October and expects to complete the transition by the end of December 2016.

The three new groups will be supported by the existing Transformation and Corporate Services areas.

A chart showing the senior management personnel of HMRC and organisational structure (as at May 2016) is available at www.gov.uk/government/up loads/system/uploads/attachment_data/file/524709/HMRC_organisation_cha rt_May_2016.pdf.

Tax Office Directory

Offices are shown under the Area name with Compliance and Service Offices identified accordingly.

Generally, post has to be addressed to one particular Office within the Area. Telephone enquiries generally go to call centres although some Compliance and Employers Offices have direct telephone access. Offices will supply direct telephone numbers when initiating or responding to correspondence, etc.

Corporation tax numbers

Corporation tax customers can contact HMRC by phone on 0300 200 3410 (+44 151 268 0571 if calling from abroad) where calls are handled by dedicated contact centre teams. If the enquiry cannot be dealt with at this first point of contact, it will be referred to and dealt with by a dedicated operations team, who will contact you where necessary. The telephone numbers for each corporation tax office are reflected in the Tax Offices section that follows. The helpline is open Mon-Fri, 8.00am–6.00pm. (The best times to call when lines may be less busy are between 8.00am–9.00am and 5.00pm–6.00pm.)

HMRC PO Box addresses for post

In May 2011, HMRC introduced PO Boxes to make it easier to send them clients' PAYE and Self-Assessment forms and letters for individuals and employees. HMRC reports that this gives agents clarity on addresses.

You can write to HMRC at the postal address shown on the most recent correspondence you have received from them. If HMRC has not written to you or your client recently, the following addresses may be used.

For all Income Tax queries except complaints:
HM Revenue and Customs
Pay As You Earn and Self-Assessment
BX9 1AS
United Kingdom
For Corporation Tax queries:
HM Revenue and Customs
Corporation Tax Services
BX9 1AX
Please note that courier deliveries to an HMRC address with a PO box or BX postcode should go to:
HM Revenue and Customs
Benton Park View
Newcastle upon Tyne
NE98 1ZZ

HMRC Enquiry Centres (replaced by new service)

In 2014, HMRC introduced a new service for customers needing extra help with their taxes, tax credits and child benefit entitlements. The service aims to identify those with additional needs and offer them the support that suits them best, whether by phone or in person at a place convenient to them. It replaced HMRC's network of enquiry centres, which closed on 30 June 2014.

There are several elements to the service:

- HMRC helpline staff will identify when a customer needs extra help, and direct them to the most appropriate tailored service;
- specialist phone advisers will take the time to resolve tax and tax credits queries in-depth, accessing experts from different parts of HMRC during the call, so that customers will not have to speak to multiple advisers;

- where a face-to-face meeting is most appropriate, a new team of mobile advisers will arrange to meet customers at convenient locations in the community, or at their home; and
- HMRC will work more closely with voluntary and community sector organisations to make it easier for such organisations to direct customers needing extra help to HMRC, and to enable HMRC to direct customers to appropriate voluntary organisations where the customers need independent advice or someone to act on their behalf.

The telephone and mobile advisory service is available through the normal helplines. Also see www.gov.uk/dealing-hmrc-additional-needs/overview.

General notes

There are still some offices in the Greater London area, mainly dealing with Compliance or Corporation Tax matters. Otherwise, a separate list of telephone contact numbers for individuals in Greater London, who do not know their correct Office details, is shown after the Tax Office list.

A list of Agent Priority Access contacts is also included.

Offices that have letterboxes or posting facilities are identified thus: (L). (D) denotes there is some disabled provision, but it is best to contact the office concerned to ascertain the nature of that provision. Where applicable DX numbers are shown for HMRC offices.

Tax offices for England, Wales, Scotland and Northern Ireland are shown on pages 5–46.

Recovery (Tax Collection) Offices information is shown on page 73–75.

Full details of Specialist Tax Functions and Stamp Offices are shown on pages 77 and 105.

Separate pages show contact details for Tax Tribunals.

Tax Offices in England, Wales, Scotland and Northern Ireland

BARNSLEY 2
(See Leics & Northants Area (Claims). See page 61.)

BARNSTAPLE 2
(See Leics & Northants Area (Claims). See page 61.)

419 **BEDS AND WEST HERTS AREA (BEDFORD CHAILEY)**

Customer Operations
PAYE and Self-Assessment
Lynx House
1 Northern Road
Cosham
Portsmouth PO6 3XA
Tel: 0300 200 3300
Textphone: 0300 200 3319
Tel (from abroad): +44 1355 359 022

419 **BEDS AND WEST HERTS AREA (BEDFORD)**

Customer Operations
PAYE and Self-Assessment
Lynx House
1 Northern Road
Cosham
Portsmouth PO6 3XA
Tel: 0300 200 3300
Textphone: 0300 200 3319
Tel (from abroad): +44 1355 359 022

438 **BEDS AND WEST HERTS AREA (COMPLIANCE)**

Aspect Gate
166 College Road
Harrow
HA1 1BH
Tel: 0300 200 3410
Tel (from abroad): +44 151 268 0571

419 **BEDS AND WEST HERTS AREA (EMPLOYERS)**

Customer Operations Employer Office
BP4009
Chillingham House
Benton Park View
Newcastle-upon-Tyne NE98 1ZZ
Tel: 0300 200 3200
Fax: 0191 285 4332/0300 052 3030

419 **BEDS AND WEST HERTS AREA (HEMEL HEMPSTEAD)**

Customer Operations
PAYE and Self-Assessment
Lynx House
1 Northern Road
Cosham
Portsmouth PO6 3XA
Tel: 0300 200 3300
Textphone: 0300 200 3319
Tel (from abroad): +44 1355 359 022

419 **BEDS AND WEST HERTS AREA (LUTON KING)**

Customer Operations
PAYE and Self-Assessment
Lynx House
1 Northern Road
Cosham
Portsmouth PO6 3XA
Tel: 0300 200 3300
Textphone: 0300 200 3319
Tel (from abroad): +44 1355 359 022

419 **BEDS AND WEST HERTS AREA (ST ALBANS)**

Customer Operations
PAYE and Self-Assessment

Lynx House
1 Northern Road
Cosham
Portsmouth PO6 3XA
Tel: 0300 200 3300
Textphone: 0300 200 3319
Tel (from abroad): +44 1355
359 022

419 BEDS AND WEST HERTS AREA (SELF-EMPLOYED)

Customer Operations
St Clare House
Princes Street
Ipswich IP1 1LW
Tel: 0300 200 3300
Tel (from abroad): +44 1355
359 022
Textphone: 0300 200 3319

419 BEDS AND WEST HERTS AREA (SERVICE)

Chailey House
Cardington Road
Bedford MK42 0YS
Tel: 0300 200 3300
(L) (D)

419 BEDS AND WEST HERTS AREA (WATFORD)

Customer Operations
PAYE and Self-Assessment
Lynx House
1 Northern Road
Cosham
Portsmouth PO6 3XA
Tel: 0300 200 3300
Textphone: 0300 200 3319
Tel (from abroad): +44 1355
359 022

BELFAST 6
(See Leics & Northants Area (Claims). See page 61.)

610 BERKSHIRE AREA (COMPLIANCE)

Aspect Gate
166 College Road
Harrow HA1 1BH
Tel: 0300 200 3410

686 BERKSHIRE AREA (LONDON SA)

Sapphire Plaza
Watlington Street
Reading RG1 4TA
Tel: 0300 200 3300
Tel (from abroad): +44 135
535 9022
Textphone: 0300 200 3319

592 BERKSHIRE AREA (NEWBURY)

Sapphire Plaza
Watlington Street
Reading RG1 4TA
Tel: 0300 200 3300
Tel (from abroad): +44 135
535 9022
Textphone: 0300 200 3319

592 BERKSHIRE AREA (SERVICE)

Sapphire Plaza
Watlington Street
Reading RG1 4TA
Tel: 0300 200 3300
Tel (from abroad): +44 135
535 9022
Textphone: 0300 200 3319

592 BERKSHIRE AREA (SLOUGH)

Sapphire Plaza
Watlington Street
Reading RG1 4TE
Tel: 0300 200 3300
Tel (from abroad): +44 135
535 9022
Textphone: 0300 0200 3319

592 BERKSHIRE AREA (WOKING)

Sapphire Plaza
Watlington Street
Reading RG1 4TE
Tel: 0300 200 3300
Tel (from abroad): +44 135
535 9022
Textphone: 0300 200 3319

BIRKENHEAD 3
*(See Leics & Northants Area
(Claims). See page 61.)*

068/09 **BIRMINGHAM & SOLIHULL
AREA (CPR TEAM)**

City Centre House
30 Union Street
Birmingham B2 4AD
Tel: 0300 200 3300

450 **BIRMINGHAM & SOLIHULL
AREA (COMPLIANCE)**

Nelson House
Prince of Wales Road
Norwich NR1 1DR
Tel: 0300 200 3410
(L)

068 **BIRMINGHAM & SOLIHULL
AREA (EMPLOYERS)**

Customer Operations Employer
Office
BP4009
Chillingham House
Benton Park View
Newcastle-upon-Tyne NE98
1ZZ
Tel: 0300 200 3200
Fax: 0191 285 4332/0300 052
3030

068 **BIRMINGHAM & SOLIHULL
AREA (SERVICE)**

City Centre House
30 Union Street
Birmingham B2 4AD
Tel: 0300 200 3300
(L) (D)

BOLTON 3
*(See Leics & Northants Area
(Claims). See page 61.)*

034 **BRISTOL & N SOMERSET
AREA (BATH)**

Southgate House
Southgate Street
Gloucester GL1 1DL
Tel: 0300 200 3300

Tel (from abroad): +44 135
535 9022
Textphone: 0300 200 3319

049 **BRISTOL & N SOMERSET
AREA (BOURNEMOUTH)
(EMPLOYERS)**

Customer Operations Employer
Office
BP4009
Chillingham House
Benton Park View
Newcastle-upon-Tyne NE98
1ZZ
Tel: 0300 200 3200
Fax: 0191 285 4332/0300 052
3030

036 **BRISTOL & N SOMERSET
AREA (COMPLIANCE)**

Crown House
11 Regent Hill
Brighton BN1 3ER
Tel: 0300 200 3410

034 **BRISTOL & N SOMERSET
AREA (EMPLOYERS)**

Customer Operations Employer
Office
BP4009
Chillingham House
Benton Park View
Newcastle-upon-Tyne NE98
1ZZ
Tel: 0300 200 3200
Fax: 0191 285 4332/0300 052
3030

034 **BRISTOL & N SOMERSET
AREA (SERVICE)**

Customer Operations
Southgate House
Southgate Street
Gloucester GL1 1DL
Tel: 0300 200 3300
Tel (from abroad): +44 135
535 9022
Textphone: 0300 200 3319
(L) (D)

Tax Offices

034 **BRISTOL & N SOMERSET AREA (WESTON-SUPER-MARE)**

Customer Operations
Southgate House
Southgate Street
Gloucester GL1 1DL
Tel: 0300 200 3300
Tel (from abroad): +44 135 535 9022
Textphone: 0300 200 3319
(L) (D)

126 **CAMBS AREA (CAMBRIDGE)**
Post to:

Customer Operations
PAYE and Self-Assessment
Lynx House
1 Northern Road
Cosham
Portsmouth PO6 3XA
Tel: 0300 200 3300
Textphone: 0300 200 3319
Tel (from abroad): +44 1355 359 022

570 **CAMBS AREA (COMPLIANCE)**

CT Operations (Ipswich Group)
St Clare House
Princes Street
Ipswich IP1 1LW
Tel: 0300 200 3410

126 **CAMBS AREA (EMPLOYERS)**

Customer Operations Employer Office
BP4009
Chillingham House
Benton Park View
Newcastle-upon-Tyne NE98 1ZZ
Tel: 0300 200 3200
Fax: 0191 285 4332/0300 052 3030

126 **CAMBS AREA (HUNTINGDON)**

Customer Operations
PAYE and Self-Assessment
Lynx House
1 Northern Road
Cosham
Portsmouth PO6 3XA
Tel: 0300 200 3300
Textphone: 0300 200 3319
Tel (from abroad): +44 1355 359 022

126 **CAMBS AREA (PETERBOROUGH)**

Customer Operations
PAYE and Self-Assessment
Lynx House
1 Northern Road
Cosham
Portsmouth PO6 3XA
Tel: 0300 200 3300
Textphone: 0300 200 3319
Tel (from abroad): +44 1355 359 022

126 **CAMBS AREA (SELF-EMPLOYED)**

Customer Operations
Self-assessment
St Clare House
Princes Street
Ipswich IP1 1LW
Tel: 0300 200 3300
Tel (from abroad): +44 135 535 9022
Textphone: 0300 200 3319

126 **CAMBS AREA (SERVICE)**

Customer Operations
PAYE and Self-Assessment
Lynx House
1 Northern Road
Cosham
Portsmouth PO6 3XA
Tel: 0300 200 3300
Textphone: 0300 200 3319
Tel (from abroad): +44 1355 359 022

623 **CENTRAL LONDON AREA (COMPLIANCE)**

Ground Floor
Euston Tower
286 Euston Road
London NW1 3UH
Tel: 0300 200 3410
(D)

301 **CENTRAL LONDON AREA (SERVICE)**

Euston Tower
286 Euston Road
London NW1 3UH
Tel: 0300 200 3300
(D)

388 **CENTRAL YORKSHIRE AREA (COMPLIANCE)**

Blackburn House
Old Hall Street
Hanley
Stoke-on-Trent ST1 3BS
Tel: 0300 200 3410
(L)

567 **CENTRAL YORKSHIRE AREA (DEWSBURY)**

Customer Operations
Centenary Court
1 St Blaise Way
Bradford BD1 4YL
Tel: 0300 200 3300

567 **CENTRAL YORKSHIRE AREA (EMPLOYERS)**

BP4009
Chillingham House
Benton Park View
Newcastle-upon-Tyne NE98 1ZZ
Tel: 0300 200 3200
Fax: 0191 285 4332/0300 052 3030
(D)

567 **CENTRAL YORKSHIRE AREA (PONTEFRACT)**

Customer Operations
Centenary Court
1 St Blaise Way

Bradford BD1 4YL
Tel: 0300 200 3300

567 **CENTRAL YORKSHIRE AREA (SERVICE)**

Castle House
31 Lisbon Street
Leeds LS1 4SA
Tel: 0300 200 3300
(L) (D)

567 **CENTRAL YORKSHIRE AREA (WAKEFIELD)**

Customer Operations
Centenary Court
1 St Blaise Way
Bradford BD1 4YL
Tel: 0300 200 3300

961/09 **CENTRE 1 AREA (CPR TEAM) EAST KILBRIDE**
(See Glasgow CPR team)

976 **CENTRE 1 AREA (COMPLIANCE)**

Queensway House
Stewartfield Way
East Kilbride
Glasgow G79 1AA
Tel: 0300 200 3410
DX:500150 East Kilbride 2
(D)

961/875 **CENTRE 1 AREA (EMPLOYERS)**

Customer Operations Employer Office
BP4009
Chillingham House
Benton Park View
Newcastle-upon-Tyne NE98 1ZZ
Tel: 0300 200 3200
Fax: 0191 285 4332/0300 052 3030

875 **CENTRE 1 AREA (SERVICE)**
(formerly London Provincial Glasgow Blythswood)

Queensway House
Stewartfield Way

East Kilbride
Glasgow G79 1AA
Tel: 0300 200 3300

961　**CENTRE 1 AREA (SERVICE)**

Queensway House
Stewartfield Way
East Kilbride
Glasgow G79 1AA
Tel: 0300 200 3300
(D)

951/09　**CHAPEL WHARF AREA
(COMPLEX PERSONAL RE-
TURN TEAM)**

3rd Floor
Trinity Bridge House
2 Dearmans Place
Salford M3 5BS
Tel: 0300 200 3300
(D)

923　**CHAPEL WHARF AREA
(COMPLIANCE)**

Trinity Bridge House
2 Dearmans Place
Salford M3 5BS
Tel: 0300 200 3300
(D)

951　**CHAPEL WHARF AREA
(EMPLOYERS)**

Customer Operations Employer
Office
BP4009
Chillingham House
Benton Park View
Newcastle-upon-Tyne NE98
1ZZ
Tel: 0300 200 3200
Fax: 0191 285 4332/0300 052
3030

951　**CHAPEL WHARF AREA
(SERVICE)**

Trinity Bridge House
2 Dearmans Place
Salford M3 5BS
Tel: 0300 200 3300
(D)

680　**CITY OF LONDON AREA
(COMPLIANCE)**

13th Floor
Euston Tower
286 Euston Road
London NW1 3UN
Tel: 0300 200 3410
(D)

305　**CITY OF LONDON AREA
(SERVICE)**

Euston Tower
286 Euston Road
London NW1 3UN
Tel: 0300 200 3300
(D)

**CORNWALL & PLYMOUTH
AREA (CLAIMS)**
*(Formerly St Austell 2 (IRO).
See page 61.)*

474　**CORNWALL & PLYMOUTH
AREA (COMPLIANCE)**

Crown House
11 Regent Hill
Brighton BN1 3ER
Tel: 0300 200 3410

470　**CORNWALL & PLYMOUTH
AREA (EMPLOYERS)**

Customer Operations Employer
Office
BP4009
Chillingham House
Benton Park View
Newcastle-upon-Tyne NE98
1ZZ
Tel: 0300 200 3200
Fax: 0191 285 4332/0300 052
3030

470　**CORNWALL & PLYMOUTH
AREA (LAUNCESTON)**

Customer Operations
Southgate House
Southgate Street
Gloucester GL1 1DL
Tel: 0300 200 3300
Tel (from abroad): +44 135
535 9022

Textphone: 0300 200 3319
(L) (D)

470 **CORNWALL & PLYMOUTH AREA (PENZANCE)**

Customer Operations
Southgate House
Southgate Street
Gloucester GL1 1DL
Tel: 0300 200 3300
Tel (from abroad): +44 135 535 9022
Textphone: 0300 200 3319
(L) (D)

842 **CORNWALL & PLYMOUTH AREA (RRTC)**

The Apex
2 Brest Road
Derriford Business Park
Plymouth PL6 5XX
Tel: 0300 200 3300

470 **CORNWALL & PLYMOUTH AREA (REDRUTH)**

Customer Operations
Southgate House
Southgate Street
Gloucester GL1 1DL
Tel: 0300 200 3300
Tel (from abroad): +44 135 535 9022
Textphone: 0300 200 3319
(L) (D)

470 **CORNWALL & PLYMOUTH AREA (ST AUSTELL)**

Customer Operations
Southgate House
Southgate Street
Gloucester GL1 1DL
Tel: 0300 200 3300
Tel (from abroad): +44 135 535 9022
Textphone: 0300 200 3319
(L) (D)

470 **CORNWALL & PLYMOUTH AREA (SERVICE)**

Customer Operations
Southgate House

Southgate Street
Gloucester GL1 1DL
Tel: 0300 200 3300
Tel (from abroad): +44 135 535 9022
Textphone: 0300 200 3319
(L) (D)

470 **CORNWALL & PLYMOUTH AREA (TRURO)**

Customer Operations
Southgate House
Southgate Street
Gloucester GL1 1DL
Tel: 0300 200 3300
Tel (from abroad): +44 135 535 9022
Textphone: 0300 200 3319
(L) (D)

783 **CUMBRIA AREA (CARLISLE)**

Customer Operations Employer Office
BP4009
Chillingham House
Benton Park View
Newcastle-upon-Tyne NE98 1ZZ
Tel: 0300 200 3200
Fax: 0191 285 4332/0300 052 3030

356 **CUMBRIA AREA (COMPLIANCE)**

Caledonian House
Greenmarket
Dundee DD1 4QX
Tel: 0300 200 3410

783 **CUMBRIA AREA (EMPLOYERS)**

Customer Operations
Employer Team
BP 4009
Chillingham House
Benton Park View
Newcastle-upon-Tyne NE98 1ZZ
Tel: 0300 200 3200
Fax: 0191 285 4332/0300 052 3030

783 **CUMBRIA AREA (FURNESS)**

Customer Operations
Room BP4101
Tynemouth House
Benton Park View
Longbenton
Newcastle-upon-Tyne NE98
1ZZ
Tel: 0300 200 3300
Textphone: 0300 200 3319
From abroad: +44 135 535
9022

783 **CUMBRIA AREA (KENDAL)**

Customer Operations
Room BP4101
Tynemouth House
Benton Park View
Longbenton
Newcastle-upon-Tyne NE98
1ZZ
Tel: 0300 200 3300
Textphone: 0300 200 3319
From abroad: +44 135 535
9022

070 **DEVON AREA
(BARNSTAPLE)**

Customer Operations
Southgate House
Southgate Street
Gloucester GL1 1DL
Tel: 0300 200 3300
Tel (from abroad): +44 135
535 9022
Textphone: 0300 200 3319
(L) (D)

070 **DEVON AREA (BIDEFORD)**

Customer Operations
Southgate House
Southgate Street
Gloucester GL1 1DL
Tel: 0300 200 3300
Tel (from abroad): +44 135
535 9022
Textphone: 0300 200 3319
(L) (D)

071 **DEVON AREA
(COMPLIANCE)**

Crown House
11 Regent Hill
Brighton BN1 3ER
Tel: 0300 200 3410

070 **DEVON AREA
(EMPLOYERS)**

Customer Operations Employer
Office
BP4009
Chillingham House
Benton Park View
Newcastle-upon-Tyne NE98
1ZZ
Tel: 0300 200 3200
Fax: 0191 285 4332/0300 052
3030

070 **DEVON AREA (HARROW
SA)**

PO Box 310
Tor Hill House
Torquay TQ2 5WF
Tel: 0300 200 3300

070 **DEVON AREA (NEWTON
ABBOT)**

Customer Operations Employer
Office
BP4009
Chillingham House
Benton Park View
Newcastle-upon-Tyne NE98
1ZZ
Tel: 0300 200 3200
Fax: 0191 285 4332/0300 052
3030

070 **DEVON AREA (SERVICE)**

Customer Operations
Southgate House
Southgate Street
Gloucester GL1 1DL
Tel: 0300 200 3300
Tel (from abroad): +44 135
535 9022
Textphone: 0300 200 3319
(L) (D)

070 **DEVON AREA (TORQUAY)**

Customer Operations
Southgate House
Southgate Street
Gloucester GL1 1DL
Tel: 0300 200 3300
Tel (from abroad): +44 135
535 9022
Textphone: 0300 200 3319
(L) (D)

578 **DORSET & S WILTS AREA
(COMPLIANCE)**

Crown House
11 Regent Hill
Brighton BN1 3ER
Tel: 0300 200 3410

503 **DORSET & S WILTS AREA
(DORCHESTER)**

Customer Operations
PAYE and Self-assessment
Lynx House
1 Northern Road
Cosham
Portsmouth PO6 3XA
Tel: 0300 200 3300

503 **DORSET & S WILTS AREA
(EMPLOYERS)**

Customer Operations Employer
Office
BP4009
Chillingham House
Benton Park View
Newcastle-upon-Tyne NE98
1ZZ
Tel: 0300 200 3200
Fax: 0191 285 4332/0300 052
3030

503 **DORSET & S WILTS AREA
(SALISBURY)**

Customer Operations
PAYE and Self-assessment
Lynx House
1 Northern Road
Cosham
Portsmouth PO6 3XA
Tel: 0300 200 3300

503 **DORSET & S WILTS AREA
(SERVICE)**

Customer Operations
PAYE and Self-assessment
Lynx House
1 Northern Road
Cosham
Portsmouth PO6 3XA
Tel: 0300 200 3300

DUNDEE 4
*(See Leics & Northants Area
(Claims). See page 61.)*

582 **E CHESHIRE & S LANCS
AREA (ASHTON-UNDER-
LYNE)**

Customer Operations
Trinity Bridge House
2 Dearmans Place
Manchester M3 5BS
Tel: 0300 200 3300
Textphone: 0300 200 3319
From abroad: +44 135 535
9022

682 **E CHESHIRE & S LANCS
AREA (COMPLIANCE)**

Blackburn House
Old Hall Street
Hanley
Stoke-on-Trent ST1 3BS
Tel: 0300 200 3410
(L) (D)

582 **E CHESHIRE & S LANCS
AREA (EMPLOYERS)**

Customer Operations
Employer Office
BP 4009
Chillingham House
Benton Park View
Newcastle-upon-Tyne NE98
1ZZ
Tel: 0300 200 3200
Fax: 0191 285 4332/0300 052
3030

582 **E CHESHIRE & S LANCS AREA (MACCLESFIELD)**
Post to:

Customer Operations
Trinity Bridge House
2 Dearmans Place
Manchester M3 5BS
Tel: 0300 200 3300
Textphone: 0300 200 3319
From abroad: +44 135 535 9022

582 **E CHESHIRE & S LANCS AREA (OLDHAM PENNINE)**

Customer Operations
Trinity Bridge House
2 Dearmans Place
Manchester M3 5BS
Tel: 0300 200 3300
Textphone:0300 200 3319
From abroad: +44 135 535 9022

582 **E CHESHIRE & S LANCS AREA (SERVICE)**

Customer Operations
Trinity Bridge House
2 Dearmans Place
Manchester M3 5BS
Tel: 0300 200 3300
Textphone: 0300 200 3319
From abroad: +44 135 535 9022

581/09 **E HANTS & ISLE OF WIGHT AREA (CPR TEAM)**

Room BP4009
Chillingham House
Benton Park View
Newcastle-upon-Tyne NE98 1ZZ
Tel: 0300 200 3200

486 **E HANTS & ISLE OF WIGHT AREA (COMPLIANCE)**

Crown House
11 Regent Hill
Brighton BN1 3ER
Tel: 0300 200 3410

581 **E HANTS & ISLE OF WIGHT AREA (EMPLOYERS)**

Room BP4009
Chillingham House
Benton Park View
Newcastle-upon-Tyne NE98 1ZZ
Tel: 0300 200 3200
Fax: 0191 285 4332/0300 052 3030

581 **E HANTS & ISLE OF WIGHT AREA (ISLE OF WIGHT)**

Customer Operations
PAYE and Self-Assessment
Lynx House
1 Northern Road
Cosham
Portsmouth PO6 3XA
Tel: 0300 200 3300
Textphone: 0300 200 3319
Tel (from abroad): +44 1355 359 022

581 **E HANTS & ISLE OF WIGHT AREA (PORTSMOUTH MARITIME)**

Customer Operations
PAYE and Self-Assessment
Lynx House
1 Northern Road
Cosham
Portsmouth PO6 3XA
Tel: 0300 200 3300
Textphone: 0300 200 3319
Tel (from abroad): +44 1355 359 022

581 **E HANTS & ISLE OF WIGHT AREA (SERVICE)**

Customer Operations
PAYE and Self-Assessment
Lynx House
1 Northern Road
Cosham
Portsmouth PO6 3XA
Tel: 0300 200 3300
Textphone: 0300 200 3319
Tel (from abroad): +44 1355 359 022

084   **E HERTS & W ESSEX AREA (COMPLIANCE)**

Crown House
11 Regent Hill
Brighton BN1 3ER
Tel: 0300 200 3410

321   **E HERTS & W ESSEX AREA (EMPLOYERS)**

Customer Operations
Employer Team
BP 4009
Chillingham House
Benton Park View
Newcastle-upon-Tyne NE98 1ZZ
Tel: 0300 200 3200
Fax: 0191 285 4332/0300 052 3030

321   **E HERTS & W ESSEX AREA (HARLOW)**

Customer Operations
PAYE and Self-assessment
Lynx House
1 Northern Road
Cosham
Portsmouth PO6 3XA
Tel: 0300 200 3300

321   **E HERTS & W ESSEX AREA (HATFIELD)**

Customer Operations
PAYE and Self-assessment
Lynx House
1 Northern Road
Cosham
Portsmouth PO6 3XA
Tel: 0300 200 3300

321   **E HERTS & W ESSEX AREA (HERTFORD)**

Customer Operations
PAYE and Self-assessment
Lynx House
1 Northern Road
Cosham
Portsmouth PO6 3XA
Tel: 0300 200 3300

321   **E HERTS & W ESSEX AREA (HITCHIN)**

Customer Operations
PAYE and Self-assessment
Lynx House
1 Northern Road
Cosham
Portsmouth PO6 3XA
Tel: 0300 200 3300

321   **E HERTS & W ESSEX AREA (SERVICE)**

Customer Operations
PAYE and Self-assessment
Lynx House
1 Northern Road
Cosham
Portsmouth PO6 3XA
Tel: 0300 200 3300

106   **E LANCS AREA (ACCRINGTON)**

Trinity Bridge House
2 Dearmans Place
Salford
Manchester M3 5BS
Tel: 0300 200 3300

106   **E LANCS AREA (BURNLEY)**

Trinity Bridge House
2 Dearmans Place
Salford
Manchester M3 5BS
Tel: 0300 200 3300

095   **E LANCS AREA (CT ONLY)**

Blackburn House
Old Hall Street
Hanley
Stoke-on-Trent ST1 3BS
Tel: 0300 200 3410
(L)

106   **E LANCS AREA (EMPLOYERS)**

Customer Operations
Employer Office
BP 4009
Chillingham House
Benton Park View

Newcastle-upon-Tyne NE98
1ZZ
Tel: 0300 200 3200
Fax: 0191 285 4332/0300 052
3030

106   E LANCS AREA (PENDLE)

Trinity Bridge House
2 Dearmans Place
Salford
Manchester M3 5BS
Tel: 0300 200 3300

**106   E LANCS AREA
(ROCHDALE)**

Trinity Bridge House
2 Dearmans Place
Salford
Manchester M3 5BS
Tel: 0300 200 3300

106   E LANCS AREA (SERVICE)

Trinity Bridge House
2 Dearmans Place
Salford
Manchester M3 5BS
Tel: 0300 200 3300

733   EAST LONDON AREA (CT)

Euston Tower
286 Euston Road
London NW1 3UH
Tel: 0300 200 3410

**717   EAST LONDON AREA
(ROMFORD)**

Customer Operations
PAYE and Self-Assessment
Lynx House
1 Northern Road
Cosham
Portsmouth PO6 3XA
Tel: 0300 200 3300
Textphone: 0300 200 3319
Tel (from abroad): +44 1355
359 022

**717   EAST LONDON AREA
(SERVICE)**

Customer Operations
PAYE and Self-Assessment
Lynx House
1 Northern Road
Cosham
Portsmouth PO6 3XA
Tel: 0300 200 3300
Textphone: 0300 200 3319
Tel (from abroad): +44 1355
359 022

**717   EAST LONDON AREA
(STRATFORD)**

Customer Operations
PAYE and Self-Assessment
Lynx House
1 Northern Road
Cosham
Portsmouth PO6 3XA
Tel: 0300 200 3300
Textphone: 0300 200 3319
Tel (from abroad): +44 1355
359 022

**717   EAST LONDON AREA
(WALTHAMSTOW)**

Customer Operations
PAYE and Self-Assessment
Lynx House
1 Northern Road
Cosham
Portsmouth PO6 3XA
Tel: 0300 200 3300
Textphone: 0300 200 3319
Tel (from abroad): +44 1355
359 022

FALKIRK 2
*(See Leics & Northants Area
(Claims). See page 61.)*

**961/09   GLASGOW (COMPLEX PER-
SONAL RETURN TEAM)**
Office now closed.

GLENROTHES IRO
*(See Leics & Northants Area
(Claims). See page 61.)*

214 **GLOS AND N WILTSHIRE AREA (CHELTENHAM)**

Southgate House
Southgate Street
Gloucester GL1 1DL
Tel: 0300 200 3300

214 **GLOS AND N WILTSHIRE AREA (CHIPPENHAM)**

Southgate House
Southgate Street
Gloucester GL1 1DL
Tel: 0300 200 3300

066 **GLOS AND N WILTSHIRE AREA (COMPLIANCE)**

Crown House
11 Regent Hill
Brighton BN1 3ER
Tel: 0300 200 3410

214 **GLOS AND N WILTSHIRE AREA (EMPLOYERS)**

Customer Operations Employer
Office
BP4009
Chillingham House
Benton Park View
Newcastle-upon-Tyne NE98
1ZZ
Tel: 0300 200 3200
Fax: 0191 285 4332/0300 052
3030

214 **GLOS AND N WILTSHIRE AREA (SERVICE)**

Southgate House
Southgate Street
Gloucester GL1 1DL
Tel: 0300 200 3300

214 **GLOS AND N WILTSHIRE AREA (STROUD)**

Southgate House
Southgate Street
Gloucester GL1 1DL
Tel: 0300 200 3300

214 **GLOS AND N WILTSHIRE AREA (SWINDON)**

Southgate House
Southgate Street
Gloucester GL1 1DL
Tel: 0300 200 3300

974 **GREATER BELFAST AREA (CLAIMS)**
(Formerly Belfast 7 IRO.. See page 61.)

933 **GREATER BELFAST AREA (COMPLIANCE)**

Ruby House
8 Ruby Place
Aberdeen AB10 1ZP
Tel: 0300 200 3410
Fax: 01224 401 734/0300 054
3889

925 **GREATER BELFAST AREA (EMPLOYERS)**

Room BP4009
Chillingham House
Benton Park View
Newcastle-upon-Tyne NE98
1ZZ
Tel: 0300 200 3200
Fax: 0191 285 4332/0300 052
3030
(D)

925 **GREATER BELFAST AREA (SERVICE)**

Beaufort House
31 Wellington Place
Belfast BT1 6BH
Tel: 0300 200 3300
(D)

HULL 4
(See Leics & Northants Area (Claims). See page 61.)

391 **HUMBER AREA (EMPLOYERS)**

Customer Operations Employer
Team
BP4009
Chillingham House

Tax Offices

Benton Park View
Newcastle-upon-Tyne NE98
1ZZ
Tel: 0300 200 3200
Fax: 0191 285 4332/0300 052
3030

391 HUMBER AREA (GOOLE)

Customer Operations
Centenary Court
1 St Blaise Way
Bradford BD1 4YL
Tel: 0300 200 3300

391 HUMBER AREA (GRIMSBY)

Customer Operations
Centenary Court
1 St Blaise Way
Bradford BD1 4YL
Tel: 0300 200 3300

**391 HUMBER AREA
(SCUNTHORPE)**

Customer Operations
Centenary Court
1 St Blaise Way
Bradford BD1 4YL
Tel: 0300 200 3300

391 HUMBER AREA (SERVICE)

Customer Operations
Centenary Court
1 St Blaise Way
Bradford BD1 4YL
Tel: 0300 200 3300

577 KENT AREA (ASHFORD)

Lynx House
1 Northern Road
Cosham
Portsmouth PO6 3XA
Tel: 0300 200 3300

**577 KENT AREA
(CANTERBURY)**

Lynx House
1 Northern Road
Cosham
Portsmouth PO6 3XA
Tel: 0300 200 3300

579 KENT AREA (COMPLIANCE)

6th Floor
Southern House
Wellesley Grove
Croydon CR9 1WW
Tel: 0300 200 3410

577 KENT AREA (EMPLOYERS)

Customer Operations Employer
Office
BP4009
Chillingham House
Benton Park View
Newcastle-upon-Tyne NE98
1ZZ
Tel: 0300 200 3200
Fax: 0191 285 4332/0300 052
3030

577 KENT AREA (GRAVESEND)

Lynx House
1 Northern Road
Cosham
Portsmouth PO6 3XA
Tel: 0300 200 3300

577 KENT AREA (LONDON SA)

Lynx House
1 Northern Road
Cosham
Portsmouth PO6 3XA
Tel: 0300 200 3300

577 KENT AREA (MARGATE)
Post to:

Lynx House
1 Northern Road
Cosham
Portsmouth PO6 3XA
Tel: 0300 200 3300

577 KENT AREA (MEDWAY)

Lynx House
1 Northern Road
Cosham
Portsmouth PO6 3XA
Tel: 0300 200 3300

577 **KENT AREA (SERVICE)**

Lynx House
1 Northern Road
Cosham
Portsmouth PO6 3XA
Tel: 0300 200 3300

577 **KENT AREA (TONBRIDGE)**

Lynx House
1 Northern Road
Cosham
Portsmouth PO6 3XA
Tel: 0300 200 3300

577 **KENT AREA (TUNBRIDGE WELLS)**

Lynx House
1 Northern Road
Cosham
Portsmouth PO6 3XA
Tel: 0300 200 3300

856 **LEICS AND NORTHANTS AREA (CLAIMS)**
(Formerly Leicester 7 (IRO).
See page 61.)

110 **LEICS AND NORTHANTS AREA (COMPLIANCE)**

CT Operations (Nottingham Group)
Fitzroy House
Castle Meadow Road
Nottingham NG2 1BD
Tel: 0300 200 3410

864 **LEICS AND NORTHANTS AREA (CROYDON SA)**

Saxon House
1 Causeway Lane
Leicester LE1 4AA
Tel: 0300 200 3300

267 **LEICS AND NORTHANTS AREA (EMPLOYERS)**

Customer Operations Employer Office
BP4009
Chillingham House
Benton Park View

Newcastle-upon-Tyne NE98 1ZZ
Tel: 0300 200 3200
Fax: 0191 285 4332/0300 052 3030

892 **LEICS AND NORTHANTS AREA (IBTO)**

Saxon House
1 Causeway Lane
Leicester LE1 4AA
Tel: 0300 200 3300
(D)

267 **LEICS AND NORTHANTS AREA (KENSINGTON SA)**
(See Cornwall and Plymouth)
See page 10.

267 **LEICS AND NORTHANTS AREA (KETTERING)**

Customer Operations
Government Buildings
Ty Glas
Llanishen
Cardiff CF14 5ZA
Tel: 0300 200 3300

267 **LEICS AND NORTHANTS AREA (MELTON MOWBRAY)**

Customer Operations
Government Buildings
Ty Glas
Llanishen
Cardiff CF14 5ZA
Tel: 0300 200 3300

267 **LEICS AND NORTHANTS AREA (NORTHAMPTON)**

Customer Operations
Government Buildings
Ty Glas
Llanishen
Cardiff CF14 5ZA
Tel: 0300 200 3300

Tax Offices

206 **LEICS AND NORTHANTS AREA (RETIREMENT ANNUITY SCHEMES)**

Customer Operations
Government Buildings
Ty Glas
Llanishen
Cardiff CF14 5ZA
Tel: 0300 200 3300

267 **LEICS AND NORTHANTS AREA (SERVICE)**

Customer Operations
Government Buildings
Ty Glas
Llanishen
Cardiff CF14 5ZA
Tel: 0300 200 3300

267 **LEICS AND NORTHANTS AREA (WELLINGBOROUGH)**

Customer Operations
Government Buildings
Ty Glas
Llanishen
Cardiff CF14 5ZA
Tel: 0300 200 3300

475 **LINCS AREA (BOSTON)**

Howard House
Castlemeadow Road
Nottingham NG2 1AB
Tel: 0300 200 3300

373 **LINCS AREA (COMPLIANCE)**

CT Operations (Nottingham Group)
Fitzroy House
Castle Meadow Road
Nottingham NG2 1BD
Tel: 0300 200 3410

475 **LINCS AREA (EMPLOYERS)**

Customer Operations Employer Office
BP4009
Chillingham House
Benton Park View
Newcastle-upon-Tyne NE98 1ZZ
Tel: 0300 200 3200
Fax: 0191 285 4332/0300 052 3030

475 **LINCS AREA (GAINSBOROUGH)**

Howard House
Castle Meadow Road
Nottingham NG2 1AB
Tel: 0300 200 3300

475 **LINCS AREA (GRANTHAM)**

Howard House
Castle Meadow Road
Nottingham NG2 1AB
Tel: 0300 200 3300

475 **LINCS AREA (LOUTH)**

Howard House
Castle Meadow Road
Nottingham NG2 1AB
Tel: 0300 200 3300

475 **LINCS AREA (RETFORD)**

Howard House
Castle Meadow Road
Nottingham NG2 1AB
Tel: 0300 200 3300

475 **LINCS AREA (SERVICE)**

Howard House
Castle Meadow Road
Nottingham NG2 1AB
Tel: 0300 200 3300

475 **LINCS AREA (SPALDING)**

Howard House
Castle Meadow Road
Nottingham NG2 1AB
Tel: 0300 200 3300

539 **LISBURN AREA (COMPLIANCE)**
(Now under Greater Belfast. See page 17.)

953 **LISBURN AREA (EMPLOYERS)**

BP4009
Chillingham House
Benton Park View
Newcastle-upon-Tyne NE98 1ZZ
Tel: 0300 200 3200
Fax: 0191 285 4332/0300 052 3030

953 **LISBURN AREA (SERVICE)**

Moira House
121 Hillsborough Road
Lisburn BT28 1LA
Tel: 0300 200 3300
(D)
(Leave post at security hut)

846 **LOTHIANS AREA (CLAIMS)**
(See Leics & Northants Area (Claims). See page 61.)

846 **LOTHIANS AREA (EMPLOYERS)**

Customer Operations Employer Office
BP4009
Chillingham House
Benton Park View
Newcastle-upon-Tyne NE98 1ZZ
Tel: 0300 200 3200
Fax: 0191 285 4332/0300 052 3030

846 **LOTHIANS AREA (GLENROTHES)**

Grayfield House
5 Bankhead Avenue
Sighthill
Edinburgh EH11 4AE
Tel: 0300 200 3300

846 **LOTHIANS AREA (GRAYFIELD)**

Grayfield House
5 Bankhead Avenue
Sighthill
Edinburgh EH11 4AE
Tel: 0300 200 3300

846 **LOTHIANS AREA (PENTLAND)**

Grayfield House
5 Bankhead Avenue
Sighthill
Edinburgh EH11 4AE
Tel: 0300 200 3300

846 **LOTHIANS AREA (SERVICE)**

Grayfield House
5 Bankhead Avenue
Sighthill
Edinburgh EH11 4AE
Tel: 0300 200 3300

962 **MANCHESTER 10**
(See Leics & Northants Area (Claims). See page 61.)

421 **MANCHESTER AREA (COMPLIANCE)**

Blackburn House
Old Hall Street
Hanley
Stoke-on-Trent ST1 3BS
Tel: 0300 200 3410

080 **MANCHESTER AREA (EMPLOYERS)**

Customer Operations Employer Office
BP4009
Chillingham House
Benton Park View
Newcastle-upon-Tyne NE98 1ZZ
Tel: 0300 200 3200
Fax: 0191 285 4332/0300 052 3030

080 **MANCHESTER AREA (SERVICE)**

Trinity Bridge House
2 Dearmans Place
Salford M3 5BS
Tel: 0300 200 3300
(D)

428 **MERSEYSIDE AREA (BIRKENHEAD)**

Customer Operations
Regian House
James Street
Liverpool L75 1AA
Tel: 0300 200 3300
Textphone: 0300 200 3319
From abroad: +44 135 535 9022

423 **MERSEYSIDE AREA (COMPLIANCE)**

Blackburn House
Old Hall Street
Hanley
Stoke-on-Trent ST1 3BS
Tel: 0300 200 3410
(L) (D)

428 **MERSEYSIDE AREA (EMPLOYERS)**

BP4009
Chillingham House
Benton Park View
Newcastle-upon-Tyne NE98 1ZZ
Tel: 0300 200 3200
Fax: 0191 285 4332/0300 052 3030

428 **MERSEYSIDE AREA (SERVICE)**

Customer Operations
Regian House
James Street
Liverpool L75 1AA
Tel: 0300 200 3300
Textphone: 0300 200 3319
From abroad: +44 135 535 9022

428 **MERSEYSIDE AREA (SOUTHPORT)**

Customer Operations
Regian House
James Street
Liverpool L75 1AA
Tel: 0300 200 3300
Textphone: 0300 200 3319

From abroad: +44 135 535 9022

963 **MIDDLESBROUGH 3**
(See Leics & Northants Area (Claims). See page 61.)

693 **MIDLANDS WEST AREA (COMPLIANCE)**

Blackburn House
Old Hall Street
Hanley
Stoke-on-Trent ST1 3BS
Tel: 0300 200 3410

653 **MIDLANDS WEST AREA (EMPLOYERS)**

BP4009
Chillingham House
Benton Park View
Newcastle-upon-Tyne NE98 1ZZ
Tel: 0300 200 3200
Fax: 0191 285 4332/0300 052 3030

653 **MIDLANDS WEST AREA (SERVICE)**

Customer Operations
Bridge House
The Waterfront
Brierley Hill DY5 1XR
Tel: 0300 200 3300
Textphone: 0300 200 3319
From abroad: +44 135 535 9022
(L) (D)

916 **N IRELAND COUNTIES AREA (BALLYMENA)**

Customer Operations
Foyle House
Duncreggan Road
Londonderry BT48 0AA
Tel: 0300 200 3300
Textphone: 0300 200 3319
From abroad: +44 135 535 9022

916 **N IRELAND COUNTIES AREA (COLERAINE)**

Customer Operations
Foyle House
Duncreggan Road
Londonderry BT48 0AA
Tel: 0300 200 3300
Textphone: 0300 200 3319
From abroad: +44 135 535 9022

987 **N IRELAND COUNTIES AREA (COMPLIANCE)**

Ruby House
8 Ruby Place
Aberdeen AB10 1ZP
Tel: 0300 200 3410
Fax: 01224 401 734/0300 054 3889
(D)

916 **N IRELAND COUNTIES AREA (EMPLOYERS)**

BP4009
Chillingham House
Benton Park View
Newcastle-upon-Tyne NE98 1ZZ
Tel: 0300 200 3200
Fax: 0191 285 4332/0300 052 3030

916 **N IRELAND COUNTIES AREA (ENNISKILLEN)**

Customer Operations
Foyle House
Duncreggan Road
Londonderry BT48 0AA
Tel: 0300 200 3300
Textphone: 0300 200 3319
From abroad: +44 135 535 9022

916 **N IRELAND COUNTIES AREA (LONDON SA)**

Customer Operations
Foyle House
Duncreggan Road
Londonderry BT48 0AA
Tel: 0300 200 3300
Textphone: 0300 200 3319

From abroad: +44 135 535 9022

916 **N IRELAND COUNTIES AREA (NEWRY)**

Customer Operations
Foyle House
Duncreggan Road
Londonderry BT48 0AA
Tel: 0300 200 3300
Textphone: 0300 200 3319
From abroad: +44 135 535 9022

916 **N IRELAND COUNTIES AREA (SERVICE)**

Customer Operations
Foyle House
Duncreggan Road
Londonderry BT48 0AA
Tel: 0300 200 3300
Textphone: 0300 200 3319
From abroad: +44 135 535 9022

529 **NORFOLK AREA (COMPLIANCE)**

Nelson House
Prince of Wales Road
Norwich NR1 1DR
Tel: 0300 200 3410
(D)

531 **NORFOLK AREA (DEREHAM)**

Lynx House
1 Northern Road
Cosham
Portsmouth PO6 3XA
Tel: 0300 200 3300

531 **NORFOLK AREA (EMPLOYERS)**

Customer Operations Employer Office
BP4009
Chillingham House
Benton Park View
Newcastle-upon-Tyne NE98 1ZZ

Tax Offices

23

Tel: 0300 200 3200
Fax: 0191 285 4332/0300 052
3030

531 **NORFOLK AREA (GREAT
YARMOUTH)**

Lynx House
1 Northern Road
Cosham
Portsmouth PO6 3XA
Tel: 0300 200 3300

531 **NORFOLK AREA
(KING'S LYNN)**

Lynx House
1 Northern Road
Cosham
Portsmouth PO6 3XA
Tel: 0300 200 3300

531 **NORFOLK AREA (LONDON
SA)**

St Clare House
Princes Street
Ipswich IP1 1LW
Tel: 0300 200 3300

531 **NORFOLK AREA (SERVICE)**

Lynx House
1 Northern Road
Cosham
Portsmouth PO6 3XA
Tel: 0300 200 3300

226 **NORTH LONDON AREA
(COMPLIANCE) (CT ONLY)**

CT Operations (Harrow
Group)
Aspect Gate
166 College Road
Harrow HA1 1BH
Tel: 0300 200 3410

209 **NORTH LONDON AREA
(EDGWARE)**

Customer Operations
PAYE and Self-Assessment
Lynx House
1 Northern Road

Cosham
Portsmouth PO6 3XA
Tel: 0300 200 3300
Textphone: 0300 200 3319
Tel (from abroad): +44 1355
359 022

209 **NORTH LONDON AREA
(ENFIELD)**

Customer Operations
PAYE and Self-Assessment
Lynx House
1 Northern Road
Cosham
Portsmouth PO6 3XA
Tel: 0300 200 3300
Textphone: 0300 200 3319
Tel (from abroad): +44 1355
359 022

209 **NORTH LONDON AREA
(FINCHLEY)**

Customer Operations
PAYE and Self-Assessment
Lynx House
1 Northern Road
Cosham
Portsmouth PO6 3XA
Tel: 0300 200 3300
Textphone: 0300 200 3319
Tel (from abroad): +44 1355
359 022

209 **NORTH LONDON AREA
(HENDON)**

Customer Operations
PAYE and Self-Assessment
Lynx House
1 Northern Road
Cosham
Portsmouth PO6 3XA
Tel: 0300 200 3300
Textphone: 0300 200 3319
Tel (from abroad): +44 1355
359 022

209 **NORTH LONDON AREA
(HORNSEY)**

Customer Operations
PAYE and Self-Assessment
Lynx House
1 Northern Road

Cosham
Portsmouth PO6 3XA
Tel: 0300 200 3300
Textphone: 0300 200 3319
Tel (from abroad): +44 1355
359 022

**209   NORTH LONDON AREA
(SERVICE)**

Customer Operations
PAYE and Self-Assessment
Lynx House
1 Northern Road
Cosham
Portsmouth PO6 3XA
Tel: 0300 200 3300
Textphone: 0300 200 3319
Tel (from abroad): +44 1355
359 022

**914   NORTH WALES AREA
(BANGOR)**

Customer Operations
Government Buildings
Ty Glas
Llanishen
Cardiff CF14 5ZA
Tel: 0300 200 3300

**914   NORTH WALES AREA
(COLWYN BAY)**

Customer Operations
Government Buildings
Ty Glas
Llanishen
Cardiff CF14 5ZA
Tel: 0300 200 3300

**793   NORTH WALES AREA
(COMPLIANCE)**

Government Buildings
Ty Glas
Llanishen
Cardiff CF14 5FP
Tel: 0300 200 3410
(L) (D)

**914   NORTH WALES AREA
(EMPLOYERS)**

BP4009
Chillingham House
Benton Park View
Newcastle-upon-Tyne NE98
1ZZ
Tel: 0300 200 3200
Fax: 0191 285 4332/0300 052
3030

**914   NORTH WALES AREA
(PORTHMADOG)**

Customer Operations
Government Buildings
Ty Glas
Llanishen
Cardiff CF14 5YA
Tel: 0300 200 3300

**914   NORTH WALES AREA
(RHYL)**

Customer Operations
Government Buildings
Ty Glas
Llanishen
Cardiff CF14 5YA
Tel: 0300 200 3300

**914   NORTH WALES AREA
(SERVICE)**

Customer Operations
Government Buildings
Ty Glas
Llanishen
Cardiff CF14 5YA
Tel: 0300 200 3300

**914   NORTH WALES AREA
(WELSHPOOL)**

Customer Operations
Government Buildings
Ty Glas
Llanishen
Cardiff CF14 5YA
Tel: 0300 200 3300

455 **NORTH WEST LONDON AREA (COMPLIANCE)**

Aspect Gate
166 College Road
Harrow HA1 1BH
Tel: 0300 200 3410

461 **NORTH WEST LONDON AREA (SERVICE)**

Aspect Gate
166 College Road
Harrow HA1 1BH
Tel: 0300 200 3300
(L) (D)

585 **NORTH YORKS AREA (BRIDLINGTON)**

Customer Operations
Centenary Court
1 St Blaise Way
Bradford BD1 4YL
Tel: 0300 200 3300

791 **NORTH YORKS AREA (COMPLIANCE)**

Fitzroy House
Castle Meadow Road
Nottingham NG2 1BD
Tel: 0300 200 3410

585 **NORTH YORKS AREA (EMPLOYERS)**

BP4009
Chillingham House
Benton Park View
Newcastle-upon-Tyne NE98 1ZZ
Tel: 0300 200 3200
Fax: 0191 285 4332/0300 052 3030

585 **NORTH YORKS AREA (HARROGATE)**

Customer Operations
Centenary Court
1 St Blaise Way
Bradford BD1 4YL
Tel: 0300 200 3300

115 **NORTH YORKS AREA (LONDON SA)**

Customer Operations
Centenary Court
1 St Blaise Way
Bradford BD1 4YL
Tel: 0300 200 3300

585 **NORTH YORKS AREA (RIPON)**

Customer Operations
Centenary Court
1 St Blaise Way
Bradford BD1 4YL
Tel: 0300 200 3300

585 **NORTH YORKS AREA (SCARBOROUGH)**

Customer Operations
Centenary Court
1 St Blaise Way
Bradford BD1 4YL
Tel: 0300 200 3300

585 **NORTH YORKS AREA (SERVICE)**

Customer Operations
Centenary Court
1 St Blaise Way
Bradford BD1 4YL
Tel: 0300 200 3300

880 **NE METROPOLITAN AREA (COMPLIANCE)**

Weardale House
Washington NE37 1LW
Tel: 0300 200 3410
(D)

120 **NE METROPOLITAN AREA (EMPLOYERS)**

Customer Operations
Employers Team
BP 4009
Chillingham House
Benton Park View
Newcastle-upon-Tyne NE98 1ZZ

Tel: 0300 200 3200
Fax: 0191 285 4332/0300 052
3030

905   **NE METROPOLITAN AREA
(FILM INDUSTRY UNIT)**

BP4101
Tynemouth House
Benton Park View
Newcastle-upon-Tyne NE98
1ZZ
Tel: 0300 200 3300

120   **NE METROPOLITAN AREA
(LONDON PROVINCIAL 10)**

BP4101
Tynemouth House
Benton Park View
Newcastle-upon-Tyne NE98
1ZZ
Tel: 0300 200 3300

120   **NE METROPOLITAN AREA
(LONDON PROVINCIAL 34)**

BP4101
Tynemouth House
Benton Park View
Newcastle-upon-Tyne NE98
1ZZ
Tel: 0300 200 3300

120   **NE METROPOLITAN AREA
(SERVICE)**

BP4101
Tynemouth House
Benton Park View
Newcastle-upon-Tyne NE98
1ZZ
Tel: 0300 200 3300

120   **NE METROPOLITAN AREA
(WASHINGTON)**
(formerly Washington
Operations Office 896)

BP4101
Tynemouth House
Benton Park View
Newcastle-upon-Tyne NE98
1ZZ
Tel: 0300 200 3300

120   **NE METROPOLITAN AREA
(WASHINGTON)**
(formerly Washington
Operations Office 898)

BP4101
Tynemouth House
Benton Park View
Newcastle-upon-Tyne NE98
1ZZ
Tel: 0300 200 3300

504   **NORTHUMBRIA AREA
(ALNWICK)**

BP4101
Tynemouth House
Benton Park View
Newcastle-upon-Tyne NE98
1ZZ
Tel: 0300 200 3300

513   **NORTHUMBRIA AREA
(COMPLIANCE) (CT ONLY)**

Ruby House
8 Ruby Place
Aberdeen AB10 1ZP
Tel: 0300 200 3410
Fax: 01224 401 734/0300 054
3889

504   **NORTHUMBRIA AREA
(EMPLOYERS)**

BP4009
Chillingham House
Benton Park View
Newcastle-upon-Tyne
NE98 1ZZ
Tel: 0300 200 3200
Fax: 0191 285 4332/0300 052
3030

504   **NORTHUMBRIA AREA
(HEXHAM)**

Tynemouth House
Benton Park View
Newcastle-upon-Tyne NE98
1ZZ
Tel: 0300 200 3300

504 **NORTHUMBRIA AREA (LONDON SA)**

Tynemouth House
Benton Park View
Newcastle-upon-Tyne NE98 1ZZ
Tel: 0300 200 3300

504 **NORTHUMBRIA AREA (MORPETH)**

Tynemouth House
Benton Park View
Newcastle-upon-Tyne NE98 1ZZ
Tel: 0300 200 3300

504 **NORTHUMBRIA AREA (NEWCASTLE)**

Tynemouth House
Benton Park View
Newcastle-upon-Tyne NE98 1ZZ
Tel: 0300 200 3300

504 **NORTHUMBRIA AREA (SERVICE)**

Tynemouth House
Benton Park View
Newcastle-upon-Tyne NE98 1ZZ
Tel: 0300 200 3300

NOTTINGHAM 6
(See Leics & Northants Area (Claims). See page 61.)

NOTTINGHAM 7
(See Leics & Northants Area (Claims). See page 61.)

507 **NOTTS AND DERBYSHIRE AREA (ALFRETON)**

Howard House
Castle Meadow Road
Nottingham NG2 1AB
Tel: 0300 200 3300

532 **NOTTS AND DERBYSHIRE AREA (COMPLIANCE) (CT ONLY)**

Fitzroy House
Castle Meadow Road
Nottingham NG2 1BD
Tel: 0300 200 3410
(D)

507 **NOTTS AND DERBYSHIRE AREA (DERBY)**

Howard House
Castle Meadow Road
Nottingham NG2 1AB
Tel: 0300 200 3300

507 **NOTTS AND DERBYSHIRE AREA (EMPLOYERS)**

Customer Operations Employer Office
BP4009
Chillingham House
Benton Park View
Newcastle-upon-Tyne NE98 1ZZ
Tel: 0300 200 3200
Fax: 0191 285 4332/0300 052 3030

507 **NOTTS AND DERBYSHIRE AREA (MANSFIELD)**

Howard House
Castle Meadow Road
Nottingham NG2 1AB
Tel: 0300 200 3300

507 **NOTTS AND DERBYSHIRE AREA (NEWARK)**

Howard House
Castle Meadow Road
Nottingham NG2 1AB
Tel: 0300 200 3300

507 **NOTTS AND DERBYSHIRE AREA (SERVICE)**

Howard House
Castle Meadow Road
Nottingham NG2 1AB
Tel: 0300 200 3300

065 **NW LANCASHIRE AREA (BLACKPOOL)**

Customer Operations
Trinity Bridge House
2 Dearmans Place
Manchester M3 5BS
Tel: 0300 200 3300
Textphone: 0300 200 3319
From abroad: +44 135 535 9022

065 **NW LANCASHIRE AREA (CHORLEY)**

Trinity Bridge House
2 Dearmans Place
Salford M3 5BS
Tel: 0300 200 3300
Textphone: 0300 200 3319
From abroad: +44 135 535 9022

449 **NW LANCASHIRE AREA (COMPLIANCE)**

CT Operations
Caledonian House
Greenmarket
Dundee DD1 4QX
Tel: 0300 200 3410

065 **NW LANCASHIRE AREA (EMPLOYERS)**

Customer Operations
Employers Team
BP 4009
Chillingham House
Benton Park View
Newcastle-upon-Tyne NE98 1ZZ
Tel: 0300 200 3200
Fax: 0191 285 4332/0300 052 3030

065 **NW LANCASHIRE AREA (LANCASTER)**

Trinity Bridge House
2 Dearmans Place
Salford
Manchester M3 5BS
Tel: 0300 200 3300
Textphone: 0300 200 3319

From abroad: +44 135 535 9022

065 **NW LANCASHIRE AREA (ST ANNES)**

Trinity Bridge House
2 Dearmans Place
Salford
Manchester M3 5BS
Tel: 0300 200 3300
Textphone: 0300 200 3319
From abroad: +44 135 535 9022

065 **NW LANCASHIRE AREA (SERVICE)**

Trinity Bridge House
2 Dearmans Place
Salford
Manchester M3 5BS
Tel: 0300 200 3300
Textphone: 0300 200 3319
From abroad: +44 135 535 9022

778 **NW MIDLANDS AND SHROPS AREA (COMPLIANCE)**

Blackburn House
Old Hall Street
Hanley
Stoke-on-Trent ST1 3BS
Tel: 0300 200 3410
(L) (D)

671 **NW MIDLANDS AND SHROPS AREA (EMPLOYERS)**

Customer Operations
Employers Team
BP 4009
Chillingham House
Benton Park View
Newcastle-upon-Tyne NE98 1ZZ
Tel: 0300 200 3200
Fax: 0191 285 4332/0300 052 3030

671 **NW MIDLANDS AND SHROPS AREA (OSWESTRY)**

Crown House
Birch Street
Wolverhampton WV1 4JX
Tel: 0300 200 3300

671 **NW MIDLANDS AND SHROPS AREA (SERVICE)**

Crown House
Birch Street
Wolverhampton WV1 4JX
Tel: 0300 200 3300
(L) (D)

671 **NW MIDLANDS AND SHROPS AREA (TELFORD)**

Crown House
Birch Street
Wolverhampton WV1 4JX
Tel: 0300 200 3300

671 **NW MIDLANDS AND SHROPS AREA (WALSALL)**

Crown House
Birch Street
Wolverhampton WV1 4JX
Tel: 0300 200 3300

362 **OXON & BUCKS AREA (AYLESBURY)**

Customer Operations
Saxon House
1 Causeway Lane
Leicester LE1 4AA
Tel: 0300 200 3300
Textphone: 0300 200 3319
From abroad: +44 135 535 9022

362 **OXON & BUCKS AREA (BANBURY)**

Customer Operations
Saxon House
1 Causeway Lane
Leicester LE1 4AA
Tel: 0300 200 3300
Textphone: 0300 200 3319
From abroad: +44 135 535 9022

402 **OXON & BUCKS AREA (COMPLIANCE)**

Aspect Gate
166 College Road
Harrow HA1 1BH
Tel: 0300 200 3410
(L) (D)

362 **OXON & BUCKS AREA (EMPLOYERS)**

Customer Operations Employer Office
BP4009
Chillingham House
Benton Park View
Newcastle-upon-Tyne NE98 1ZZ
Tel: 0300 200 3200
Fax: 0191 285 4332/0300 052 3030

362 **OXON & BUCKS AREA (HIGH WYCOMBE)**

Customer Operations
Saxon House
1 Causeway Lane
Leicester LE1 4AA
Tel: 0300 200 3300
Textphone: 0300 200 3319
From abroad: +44 135 535 9022

362 **OXON & BUCKS AREA (MILTON KEYNES)**

Customer Operations
Saxon House
1 Causeway Lane
Leicester LE1 4AA
Tel: 0300 200 3300
Textphone: 0300 200 3319
From abroad: +44 135 535 9022

362 **OXON & BUCKS AREA (OXFORD)**

Customer Operations
Saxon House
1 Causeway Lane
Leicester LE1 4AA
Tel: 0300 200 3300
Textphone: 0300 200 3319

From abroad: +44 135 535 9022

362 **OXON & BUCKS AREA (SELF-EMPLOYED)**

Customer Operations
Saxon House
1 Causeway Lane
Leicester LE1 4AA
Tel: 0300 200 3300
Textphone: 0300 200 3319
From abroad: +44 135 535 9022

362 **OXON & BUCKS AREA (SERVICE)**

Customer Operations
Saxon House
1 Causeway Lane
Leicester LE1 4AA
Tel: 0300 200 3300
Textphone: 0300 200 3319
From abroad: +44 135 535 9022

PLYMOUTH 3
(See Leics & Northants Area (Claims). See page 61.)

940 **PUBLIC DEPARTMENT 1**

(South Wales Area)
Ty Glas
Llanishen
Cardiff CF14 5XZ
Tel: 02920 325 048
(D)

852 **SCOTLAND CENTRAL AREA (COATBRIDGE)**

Queensway House
East Kilbride
Glasgow G79 1AA
Tel: 0300 200 3300

817 **SCOTLAND CENTRAL AREA (COMPLIANCE)**

Cotton House
7 Cochrane Street
Glasgow G1 1HY
Tel: 0300 200 3410
(L) (D)

852 **SCOTLAND CENTRAL AREA (HAMILTON)**

Queensway House
East Kilbride
Glasgow G79 1AA
Tel: 0300 200 3300

852 **SCOTLAND CENTRAL AREA (MOTHERWELL)**

Queensway House
East Kilbride
Glasgow G79 1AA
Tel: 0300 200 3300

852 **SCOTLAND CENTRAL AREA (PAISLEY)**

Queensway House
East Kilbride
Glasgow G79 1AA
Tel: 0300 200 3300

852 **SCOTLAND CENTRAL AREA (SERVICE)**

Queensway House
East Kilbride
Glasgow G79 1AA
Tel: 0300 200 3300

825 **SCOTLAND EAST AREA (COMPLIANCE)**

Caledonian House
Greenmarket
Dundee DD1 4QX
Tel: 0300 200 3410
(L) (D)

837 **SCOTLAND EAST AREA (DUNFERMLINE)**

Queensway House
East Kilbride
Glasgow G79 1AA
Tel: 0300 200 3300

837 **SCOTLAND EAST AREA (KIRKCALDY)**

Queensway House
East Kilbride
Glasgow G79 1AA
Tel: 0300 200 3300

865 **SCOTLAND EAST AREA (LONDON SA)**

Queensway House
East Kilbride
Glasgow G79 1AA
Tel: 0300 200 3300

837 **SCOTLAND EAST AREA (PERTH)**

Queensway House
East Kilbride
Glasgow G79 1AA
Tel: 0300 200 3300

837 **SCOTLAND EAST AREA (SERVICE)**

Queensway House
East Kilbride
Glasgow G79 1AA
Tel: 0300 200 3300

985 **SCOTLAND NORTH AREA (BUCKIE)**

Queensway House
East Kilbride
Glasgow G79 1AA
Tel: 0300 200 3300

795 **SCOTLAND NORTH AREA (COMPLIANCE) (CT ONLY)**

Ruby House
8 Ruby Place
Aberdeen AB10 1ZP
Tel: 0300 200 3410
Fax: 01224 401 734/0300 054
3889
(L) (D)

985 **SCOTLAND NORTH AREA (INVERNESS)**

Queensway House
East Kilbride
Glasgow G79 1AA
Tel: 0300 200 3300

985 **SCOTLAND NORTH AREA (PETERHEAD)**

Queensway House
East Kilbride
Glasgow G79 1AA

Tel: 0300 200 3300

985 **SCOTLAND NORTH AREA (SERVICE)**

Queensway House
East Kilbride
Glasgow G79 1AA
Tel: 0300 200 3300

985 **SCOTLAND NORTH AREA (WICK)**

Queensway House
East Kilbride
Glasgow G79 1AA
Tel: 0300 200 3300

801 **SCOTLAND SOUTH AREA (FALKIRK)**

Queensway House
East Kilbride
Glasgow G79 1AA
Tel: 0300 200 3300

801 **SCOTLAND SOUTH AREA (GALASHIELS)**

Queensway House
East Kilbride
Glasgow G79 1AA
Tel: 0300 200 3300

801 **SCOTLAND SOUTH AREA (HAWICK)**

Queensway House
East Kilbride
Glasgow G79 1AA
Tel: 0300 200 3300

801 **SCOTLAND SOUTH AREA (SERVICE)**

Elgin House
20 Haymarket Yards
Edinburgh EH12 5WS
Tel: 0300 200 3300

801 **SCOTLAND SOUTH AREA (STIRLING)**

Queensway House
East Kilbride
Glasgow G79 1AA
Tel: 0300 200 3300

799 **SCOTLAND WEST AREA (AYR)**

Queensway House
East Kilbride
Glasgow G79 1AA
Tel: 0300 200 3300

820 **SCOTLAND WEST AREA (COMPLIANCE)**

Ruby House
8 Ruby Place
Aberdeen AB10 1ZP
Tel: 0300 200 3410
Fax: 01224 401 734/0300 054 3889

808 **SCOTLAND WEST AREA (CORPORATION TAX)**

Ruby House
8 Ruby Place
Aberdeen AB10 1ZP
Tel: 0300 200 3410
Fax: 01224 401 734/0300 054 3889

799 **SCOTLAND WEST AREA (DUMBARTON)**

Queensway House
East Kilbride
Glasgow G79 1AA
Tel: 0300 200 3300

799 **SCOTLAND WEST AREA (DUMFRIES)**

Queensway House
East Kilbride
Glasgow G79 1AA
Tel: 0300 200 3300

799 **SCOTLAND WEST AREA (DUNOON)**

Queensway House
East Kilbride
Glasgow G79 1AA
Tel: 0300 200 3300

799 **SCOTLAND WEST AREA (GREENOCK)**

Queensway House
East Kilbride

Glasgow G79 1AA
Tel: 0300 200 3300

799 **SCOTLAND WEST AREA (IRVINE)**

Queensway House
East Kilbride
Glasgow G79 1AA
Tel: 0300 200 3300

799 **SCOTLAND WEST AREA (ROTHESAY)**

Queensway House
East Kilbride
Glasgow G79 1AA
Tel: 0300 200 3300

799 **SCOTLAND WEST AREA (SERVICE)**

Queensway House
East Kilbride
Glasgow G79 1AA
Tel: 0300 200 3300

965 **SEFTON AREA (CLAIMS)**
(Formerly Bootle 1 (IRO). See page 61.)

077 **SEFTON AREA (COMPLIANCE)**

Blackburn House
Old Hall Street
Hanley
Stoke-on-Trent ST1 3BS
Tel: 0300 200 3410
(L) (D)

083 **SEFTON AREA (EMPLOYERS)**

BP4009
Chillingham House
Benton Park View
Newcastle-upon-Tyne NE98 1ZZ
Tel: 0300 200 3200
Fax: 0191 285 4332/0300 052 3030

840 **SEFTON AREA (LONDON SA)**

The Triad
Stanley Road
Bootle L75 1HW
Tel: 0300 200 3300

083 **SEFTON AREA (SERVICE)**

The Triad
Stanley Road
Bootle L75 1HW
Tel: 0300 200 3300
(D)

992 **SEFTON AREA (SERVICE)**

The Triad
Stanley Road
Bootle L75 1HW
Tel: 0300 200 3300
(D)

794 **SOMERSET AREA (BRIDGWATER)**

Southgate House
Southgate Street
Gloucester GL1 1DL
Tel: 0300 200 3300
Textphone: 0300 200 3319
From abroad: +44 135 535 9022

705 **SOMERSET AREA (COMPLIANCE)**

Crown House
11 Regent Hill
Brighton BN1 3ER
Tel: 0300 200 3410
(L) (D)

794 **SOMERSET AREA (EMPLOYERS)**

Customer Operations Employer Office
BP4009
Chillingham House
Benton Park View
Newcastle-upon-Tyne NE98 1ZZ
Tel: 0300 200 3200
Fax: 0191 285 4332/0300 052 3030

794 **SOMERSET AREA (FROME)**

Southgate House
Southgate Street
Gloucester GL1 1DL
Tel: 0300 200 3300

794 **SOMERSET AREA (SERVICE)**

Southgate House
Southgate Street
Gloucester GL1 1DL
Tel: 0300 200 3300
Textphone: 0300 200 3319
From abroad: +44 135 535 9022

794 **SOMERSET AREA (WELLS)**

Southgate House
Southgate Street
Gloucester GL1 1DL
Tel: 0300 200 3300
Textphone: 0300 200 3319
From abroad: +44 135 535 9022

794 **SOMERSET AREA (YEOVIL)**

Southgate House
Southgate Street
Gloucester GL1 1DL
Tel: 0300 200 3300
Textphone: 0300 200 3319
From abroad: +44 135 535 9022

224 **SOUTH EAST LONDON AREA (COMPLIANCE)**

13th Floor
Euston Tower
286 Euston Road
London NW1 3UH
Tel: 0300 200 3410

222 **SOUTH EAST LONDON AREA (SERVICE)**

Dorset House
27-45 Stamford Street
London SE1 9PY
Tel: 0300 200 3300

662 **SOUTH ESSEX AREA (BASILDON)**

Lynx House
1 Northern Road
Cosham
Portsmouth PO6 3XA
Tel: 0300 200 3300
Textphone: 0300 200 3319
From abroad: +44 135 535 9022

662 **SOUTH ESSEX AREA (CHELMSFORD)**

Lynx House
1 Northern Road
Cosham
Portsmouth PO6 3XA
Tel: 0300 200 3300
Textphone: 0300 200 3319
From abroad: +44 135 535 9022

665 **SOUTH ESSEX AREA (COMPLIANCE)**

St Clare House
Princes Street
Ipswich IP1 1RE
Tel: 0300 200 3410
(D)

662 **SOUTH ESSEX AREA (EMPLOYERS)**

Customer Operations Employer Office
BP4009
Chillingham House
Benton Park View
Newcastle-upon-Tyne NE98 1ZZ
Tel: 0300 200 3200
Fax: 0191 285 4332/0300 052 3030

662 **SOUTH ESSEX AREA (GRAYS)**

Lynx House
1 Northern Road
Cosham
Portsmouth PO6 3XA
Tel: 0300 200 3300
Textphone: 0300 200 3319

From abroad: +44 135 535 9022

662 **SOUTH ESSEX AREA (LONDON SA)**

Lynx House
1 Northern Road
Cosham
Portsmouth PO6 3XA
Tel: 0300 200 3300
Textphone: 0300 200 3319
From abroad: +44 135 535 9022

662 **SOUTH ESSEX AREA (SERVICE)**

Lynx House
1 Northern Road
Cosham
Portsmouth PO6 3XA
Tel: 0300 200 3300
Textphone: 0300 200 3319
From abroad: +44 135 535 9022

201 **SOUTH LONDON AREA (CORPORATION TAX ONLY)**

Southern House
Wellesley Grove
Croydon CR9 1WW
Tel: 0300 200 3410

948 **SOUTH WALES AREA (BRECON)**

Government Buildings
Ty Glas
Llanishen
Cardiff CF14 5YA
Tel: 0300 200 3300
Textphone: 0300 200 3319
From abroad: +44 135 535 9022

948 **SOUTH WALES AREA (CARDIFF)**

Government Buildings
Ty Glas
Llanishen
Cardiff CF14 5YA
Tel: 0300 200 3300

Textphone: 0300 200 3319
From abroad: +44 135 535 9022

192/09 SOUTH WALES AREA (COMPLEX PERSONAL RE-TURN TEAM)

1 East, Phase Two
Ty Glas
Llanishen
Cardiff CF14 5ZX
Tel: 02920 325 053
Fax: 0300 058 2467

204 SOUTH WALES AREA (COMPLIANCE)

Government Buildings
Ty Glas
Llanishen
Cardiff CF14 5FP
Tel: 0300 200 3410
(D)

948 SOUTH WALES AREA (EMPLOYERS)

BP4009
Chillingham House
Benton Park View
Newcastle-upon-Tyne NE98 1ZZ
Tel: 0300 200 3200
Fax: 0191 285 4332/0300 052 3030

948 SOUTH WALES AREA (MER-THYR TYDFIL)

Government Buildings
Ty Glas
Llanishen
Cardiff CF14 5YA
Tel: 0300 200 3300
Textphone: 0300 200 3319
From abroad: +44 135 535 9022

948 SOUTH WALES AREA (NEWPORT)

Government Buildings
Ty Glas
Llanishen
Cardiff CF14 5YA

Tel: 0300 200 3300
Textphone: 0300 200 3319
From abroad: +44 135 535 9022

075 SOUTH WALES AREA (OXFORD)

Government Buildings
Ty Glas
Llanishen
Cardiff CF14 5YA
Tel: 0300 200 3300
Textphone: 0300 200 3319
From abroad: +44 135 535 9022

948 SOUTH WALES AREA (PONTYPOOL)

Government Buildings
Ty Glas
Llanishen
Cardiff CF14 5YA
Tel: 0300 200 3300
Textphone: 0300 200 3319
From abroad: +44 135 535 9022

948 SOUTH WALES AREA (PONTYPRIDD)

Government Buildings
Ty Glas
Llanishen
Cardiff CF14 5YA
Tel: 0300 200 3300
Textphone: 0300 200 3319
From abroad: +44 135 535 9022

948 SOUTH WALES AREA (SERVICE)

Government Buildings
Ty Glas
Llanishen
Cardiff CF14 5YA
Tel: 0300 200 3300
Textphone: 0300 200 3319
From abroad: +44 135 535 9022
(D)

Tax Offices

714   **S W LONDON AREA (COMPLIANCE) (CT ONLY)**
(Moved to Scotland South area 809.)

599   **SOUTH WEST LONDON AREA (KINGSTON-UPON-THAMES)**

Customer Operations
Saxon House
1 Causeway Lane
Leicester LE1 4AA
Tel: 0300 200 3300
Textphone: 0300 200 3319
From abroad: +44 135 535 9022

599   **SOUTH WEST LONDON AREA (SERVICE)**

Bridge House
69 London Road
Twickenham TW1 3QR
Tel: 0300 200 3300
(L)

673   **SOUTH YORKSHIRE AREA (BARNSLEY)**

Customer Operations
Centenary Court
1 St Blaise Way
Bradford BD1 4YL
Tel: 0300 200 3300

673   **SOUTH YORKSHIRE AREA (CHESTERFIELD)**

Customer Operations
Centenary Court
1 St Blaise Way
Bradford BD1 4YL
Tel: 0300 200 3300
Textphone: 0300 200 3319
From abroad: +44 135 535 9022

725   **SOUTH YORKSHIRE AREA (COMPLIANCE)**

Fitzroy House
Castle Meadow Road
Nottingham NG2 1BD
Tel: 0300 200 3410

673   **SOUTH YORKSHIRE AREA (DONCASTER)**

Customer Operations
Centenary Court
1 St Blaise Way
Bradford BD1 4YL
Tel: 0300 200 3300
Textphone: 0300 200 3319
From abroad: +44 135 535 9022

673   **SOUTH YORKSHIRE AREA (EMPLOYERS)**

BP4009
Chillingham House
Benton Park View
Newcastle-upon-Tyne NE98 1ZZ
Tel: 0300 200 3200
Fax: 0191 285 4332/0300 052 3030

673   **SOUTH YORKSHIRE AREA (SERVICE)**

Customer Operations
Centenary Court
1 St Blaise Way
Bradford BD1 4YL
Tel: 0300 200 3300
Textphone: 0300 200 3319
From abroad: +44 135 535 9022

673   **SOUTH YORKSHIRE AREA (SHEFFIELD)**

Customer Operations
Centenary Court
1 St Blaise Way
Bradford BD1 4YL
Tel: 0300 200 3300
Textphone: 0300 200 3319
From abroad: +44 135 535 9022

966   **SOUTHAMPTON 6**
(See Leics & Northants Area (Claims). See page 61.)

586 **STAFFORDSHIRE AREA (BURTON-ON-TRENT)**

Customer Operations
Government Buildings
Ty Glas
Llanishen
Cardiff CF14 5YA
Tel: 0300 200 3300

586 **STAFFORDSHIRE AREA (CANNOCK)**

Customer Operations
Government Buildings
Ty Glas
Llanishen
Cardiff CF14 5YA
Tel: 0300 200 3300

687 **STAFFORDSHIRE AREA (COMPLIANCE)**

Blackburn House
Old Hall Street
Hanley
Stoke-on-Trent ST1 3BF
Tel: 0300 200 3410
(D)

586 **STAFFORDSHIRE AREA (EMPLOYERS)**

BP4009
Chillingham House
Benton Park View
Newcastle-upon-Tyne NE98 1ZZ
Tel: 0300 200 3200
Fax: 0191 285 4332/0300 052 3030

586 **STAFFORDSHIRE AREA (LEEK)**

Customer Operations
Government Buildings
Ty Glas
Llanishen
Cardiff CF14 5YA
Tel: 0300 200 3300

586 **STAFFORDSHIRE AREA (SERVICE)**

Customer Operations
Government Buildings
Ty Glas
Llanishen
Cardiff CF14 5YA
Tel: 0300 200 3300

586 **STAFFORDSHIRE AREA (STAFFORD)**

Customer Operations
Government Buildings
Ty Glas
Llanishen
Cardiff CF14 5YA
Tel: 0300 200 3300

245 **SUFFOLK & N ESSEX AREA (BURY ST EDMUNDS)**

Lynx House
1 Northern Road
Cosham
Portsmouth PO6 3XA
Tel: 0300 200 3300

245 **SUFFOLK & N ESSEX AREA (CLACTON)**

Lynx House
1 Northern Road
Cosham
Portsmouth PO6 3XA
Tel: 0300 200 3300

245 **SUFFOLK & N ESSEX AREA (COLCHESTER)**

Lynx House
1 Northern Road
Cosham
Portsmouth PO6 3XA
Tel: 0300 200 3300

346 **SUFFOLK & N ESSEX AREA (COMPLIANCE)**

CT Operations (Norfolk Group)
Nelson House
Prince of Wales Road
Norwich NR1 1DR
Tel: 0300 200 3410

245 **SUFFOLK & N ESSEX AREA (EMPLOYERS)**

Customer Operations Employer Office
BP4009
Chillingham House
Benton Park View
Newcastle-upon-Tyne NE98 1ZZ
Tel: 0300 200 3200
Fax: 0191 285 4332/0300 052 3030

245 **SUFFOLK & N ESSEX AREA (SERVICE)**

Lynx House
1 Northern Road
Cosham
Portsmouth PO6 3XA
Tel: 0300 200 3300

245 **SUFFOLK & N ESSEX AREA (SUDBURY)**

Lynx House
1 Northern Road
Cosham
Portsmouth PO6 3XA
Tel: 0300 200 3300

245 **SUFFOLK & N ESSEX AREA (WITHAM)**

Lynx House
1 Northern Road
Cosham
Portsmouth PO6 3XA
Tel: 0300 200 3300

964 **SUNDERLAND 3**
(See Leics & Northants Area (Claims). See page 61.)

765 **SURREY AND N HAMPSHIRE AREA (BASINGSTOKE)**

Grayfield House
5 Bankhead Avenue
Edinburgh EH11 4AE
Tel: 0300 200 3300
Textphone: 0300 200 3319
From abroad: +44 135 535 9022

738 **SURREY AND N HAMPSHIRE AREA (COMPLIANCE)**

6th Floor
Southern House
Wellesley Grove
Croydon CR9 1WW
Tel: 0300 200 3410

765 **SURREY AND N HAMPSHIRE AREA (EMPLOYERS)**

Customer Operations Employer Office
BP4009
Chillingham House
Benton Park View
Newcastle-upon-Tyne NE98 1ZZ
Tel: 0300 200 3200
Fax: 0191 285 4332/0300 052 3030

765 **SURREY AND N HAMPSHIRE AREA (EPSOM)**

Grayfield House
5 Bankhead Avenue
Edinburgh EH11 4AE
Tel: 0300 200 3300
Textphone: 0300 200 3319
From abroad: +44 135 535 9022

765 **SURREY AND N HAMPSHIRE AREA (SERVICE)**

Grayfield House
5 Bankhead Avenue
Edinburgh EH11 4AE
Tel: 0300 200 3300
Textphone: 0300 200 3319
From abroad: +44 135 535 9022

765 **SURREY AND N HAMPSHIRE AREA (STAINES)**

Grayfield House
5 Bankhead Avenue
Edinburgh EH11 4AE
Tel: 0300 200 3300

Textphone: 0300 200 3319
From abroad: +44 135 535
9022

765 **SURREY AND N
HAMPSHIRE AREA
(WALTON-ON-THAMES)**

Grayfield House
5 Bankhead Avenue
Edinburgh EH11 4AE
Tel: 0300 200 3300
Textphone: 0300 200 3319
From abroad: +44 135 535
9022

334 **SUSSEX AREA
(CHICHESTER)**

Queensway House
Stewartfield Way
East Kilbride
Glasgow G79 1AA
Tel: 0300 200 3300

333 **SUSSEX AREA
(COMPLIANCE)**

Crown House
11 Regent Hill
Brighton BN1 3ER
Tel: 0300 200 3410
(L)

334 **SUSSEX AREA (CRAWLEY)**

Queensway House
Stewartfield Way
East Kilbride
Glasgow G79 1AA
Tel: 0300 200 3300

334 **SUSSEX AREA (EMPLOYERS)**

Customer Operations Employer
Office
BP4009
Chillingham House
Benton Park View
Newcastle-upon-Tyne NE98
1ZZ
Tel: 0300 200 3200
Fax: 0191 285 4332/0300 052
3030

334 **SUSSEX AREA (HASTINGS)**

Queensway House
Stewartfield Way
East Kilbride
Glasgow G79 1AA
Tel: 0300 200 3300

334 **SUSSEX AREA (HORSHAM)**

Queensway House
Stewartfield Way
East Kilbride
Glasgow G79 1AA
Tel: 0300 200 3300

334 **SUSSEX AREA (LEWES)**

Queensway House
Stewartfield Way
East Kilbride
Glasgow G79 1AA
Tel: 0300 200 3300

334 **SUSSEX AREA (SERVICE)**

Queensway House
Stewartfield Way
East Kilbride
Glasgow G79 1AA
Tel: 0300 200 3300

334 **SUSSEX AREA (WORTHING)**

Queensway House
Stewartfield Way
East Kilbride
Glasgow G79 1AA
Tel: 0300 200 3300

877 **SWANSEA 3**
*(See Leics & Northants Area
(Claims). See page 61.)*

406 **TEES VALLEY AREA
(BISHOP AUCKLAND)**

Customer Operations Employer
Office
BP4009
Chillingham House
Benton Park View
Newcastle-upon-Tyne NE98
1ZZ

Tel: 0300 200 3200
Fax: 0191 285 4332/0300 052
3030

**417   TEES VALLEY AREA
        (COMPLIANCE)**

CT Operations (Norfolk
Group)
Nelson House
Prince of Wales Road
Norwich NR1 1DR
Tel: 0300 200 3410

**406   TEES VALLEY AREA
        (DARLINGTON)**

Customer Operations Employer
Office
BP4009
Chillingham House
Benton Park View
Newcastle-upon-Tyne NE98
1ZZ
Tel: 0300 200 3200
Fax: 0191 285 4332/0300 052
3030

**406   TEES VALLEY AREA
        (EMPLOYERS)**

Customer Operations
Employer Team
BP 4009
Chillingham House
Benton Park View
Newcastle-upon-Tyne NE98
1ZZ
Tel: 0300 200 3200
Fax: 0191 285 4332/0300 052
3030

**406   TEES VALLEY AREA
        (SERVICE)**

Customer Operations Employer
Office
BP4009
Chillingham House
Benton Park View
Newcastle-upon-Tyne NE98
1ZZ
Tel: 0300 200 3200
Fax: 0191 285 4332/0300 052
3030

971   **TELFORD PRIORSLEE**
       *(See Leics & Northants Area
       (Claims). See page 61.)*

709   **W LANCS & W CHESHIRE
       AREA (CHESTER)**

The Triad
Stanley Road
Bootle L75 1HS
Tel: 0300 200 3300

750   **W LANCS & W CHESHIRE
       AREA (COMPLIANCE)**

Merthyr Tydfil 2
Government Buildings
Castle Street
Merthyr Tydfil CF47 8AA
Tel: 0300 200 3410
(D)

709   **W LANCS & W CHESHIRE
       AREA (CREWE)**

The Triad
Stanley Road
Bootle L75 1HS
Tel: 0300 200 3300

709   **W LANCS & W CHESHIRE
       AREA (EMPLOYERS)**

BP4009
Chillingham House
Benton Park View
Newcastle-upon-Tyne NE98
1ZZ
Tel: 0300 200 3200
Fax: 0191 285 4332/0300 052
3030

709   **W LANCS & W CHESHIRE
       AREA (LEIGH)**

The Triad
Stanley Road
Bootle L75 1HS
Tel: 0300 200 3300

709   **W LANCS & W CHESHIRE
       AREA (NORTHWICH)**

The Triad
Stanley Road
Bootle L75 1HS

Tax Offices

Tel: 0300 200 3300

709 **W LANCS & W CHESHIRE AREA (ST HELENS)**

The Triad
Stanley Road
Bootle L75 1HS
Tel: 0300 200 3300

709 **W LANCS & W CHESHIRE AREA (SERVICE)**

The Triad
Stanley Road
Bootle L75 1HS
Tel: 0300 200 3300

709 **W LANCS & W CHESHIRE AREA (WARRINGTON)**

The Triad
Stanley Road
Bootle L75 1HS
Tel: 0300 200 3300

709 **W LANCS & W CHESHIRE AREA (WIDNES)**

The Triad
Stanley Road
Bootle L75 1HS
Tel: 0300 200 3300

709 **W LANCS & W CHESHIRE AREA (WIGAN)**

The Triad
Stanley Road
Bootle L75 1HS
Tel: 0300 200 3300

100 **W YORKS AND CRAVEN AREA (COMPLIANCE)**

Fitzroy House
Castle Meadow Road
Nottingham NG2 1BD
Tel: 0300 200 3410

072 **W YORKS AND CRAVEN AREA (EMPLOYERS)**

BP40009
Chillingham House
Benton Park View

Newcastle-upon-Tyne NE98 1ZZ
Tel: 0300 200 3300
Fax: 0191 285 4332/0300 052 3030

072 **W YORKS AND CRAVEN AREA (HALIFAX)**

Centenary Court
1 St Blaise Way
Bradford BD1 4YL
Tel: 0300 200 3300

072 **W YORKS AND CRAVEN AREA (HUDDERSFIELD)**

Centenary Court
1 St Blaise Way
Bradford BD1 4YL
Tel: 0300 200 3300

072 **W YORKS AND CRAVEN AREA (KEIGHLEY)**

Centenary Court
1 St Blaise Way
Bradford BD1 4YL
Tel: 0300 200 3300

072 **W YORKS AND CRAVEN AREA (SERVICE)**

Centenary Court
1 St Blaise Way
Bradford BD1 4YL
Tel: 0300 200 3300

073 **W YORKS AND CRAVEN AREA (SERVICE)**

Centenary Court
1 St Blaise Way
Bradford BD1 4YE
Tel: 0300 200 3300

072 **W YORKS AND CRAVEN AREA (SKIPTON)**

Centenary Court
1 St Blaise Way
Bradford BD1 4YL
Tel: 0300 200 3300

195 **WARKS & COVENTRY AREA (COMPLIANCE)**

Nelson House
Prince of Wales Road
Norwich NR1 1DR
Tel: 0300 200 3410

190 **WARKS & COVENTRY AREA (EMPLOYERS)**

Customer Operations Employer Office
BP4009
Chillingham House
Benton Park View
Newcastle-upon-Tyne NE98 1ZZ
Tel: 0300 200 3200
Fax: 0191 285 4332/0300 052 3030

190 **WARKS & COVENTRY AREA (LEAMINGTON)**

Lynx House
1 Northern Road
Cosham
Portsmouth PO6 3XA
Tel: 0300 200 3300

190 **WARKS & COVENTRY AREA (NUNEATON)**

Lynx House
1 Northern Road
Cosham
Portsmouth PO6 3XA
Tel: 0300 200 3300

190 **WARKS & COVENTRY AREA (RUGBY)**

Lynx House
1 Northern Road
Cosham
Portsmouth PO6 3XA
Tel: 0300 200 3300

190 **WARKS & COVENTRY AREA (SERVICE)**

Lynx House
1 Northern Road
Cosham
Portsmouth PO6 3XA
Tel: 0300 200 3300

190 **WARKS & COVENTRY AREA (STRATFORD-UPON-AVON)**

Lynx House
1 Northern Road
Cosham
Portsmouth PO6 3XA
Tel: 0300 200 3300

626 **WEAR AND SOUTH TYNE AREA (COMPLIANCE)**

CT Operations (Aberdeen Group)
Ruby House
8 Ruby Place
Aberdeen AB10 1ZP
Tel: 0300 200 3410

465 **WEAR AND S TYNE AREA (DURHAM)**

Customer Operations Employer Office
BP4009
Chillingham House
Benton Park View
Newcastle-upon-Tyne NE98 1ZZ
Tel: 0300 200 3200
Fax: 0191 285 4332/0300 052 3030

465 **WEAR AND SOUTH TYNE AREA (EMPLOYERS)**

Customer Operations Employer Team
BP 4009
Chillingham House
Benton Park View
Newcastle-upon-Tyne NE98 1ZZ
Tel: 0300 200 3200
Fax: 0191 285 4332/0300 052 3030

465 **WEAR AND SOUTH TYNE AREA (SERVICE)**

Customer Operations Employer Office
BP4009
Chillingham House
Benton Park View

Newcastle-upon-Tyne NE98 1ZZ
Tel: 0300 200 3200
Fax: 0191 285 4332/0300 052 3030

663 WEST HAMPSHIRE AREA (ANDOVER)

Trinity Bridge House
2 Dearmans Place
Salford M3 5BS
Tel: 0300 200 3300

664 WEST HAMPSHIRE AREA (COMPLIANCE)

CT Operations (Brighton Group)
Crown House
11 Regent Hill
Brighton BN1 3ER
Tel: 0300 200 3410

663 WEST HAMPSHIRE AREA (EMPLOYERS)

Customer Operations Employer Office
BP4009
Chillingham House
Benton Park View
Newcastle-upon-Tyne NE98 1ZZ
Tel: 0300 200 3200
Fax: 0191 285 4332/0300 052 3030

663 WEST HAMPSHIRE AREA (SERVICE)

Trinity Bridge House
2 Dearmans Place
Salford M3 5BS
Tel: 0300 200 3300

663 WEST HAMPSHIRE AREA (WINCHESTER)

Trinity Bridge House
2 Dearmans Place
Salford M3 5BS
Tel: 0300 200 3300

281 WEST LONDON AREA (COMPLIANCE) (CORPORATION TAX ONLY)

13th Floor
Euston Tower
286 Euston Road
London NW1 3UH
Tel: 0300 200 3410

193 WEST LONDON AREA (EALING BROADWAY TAX SHOP)

7 High Street
Ealing Broadway
London W5 5DJ
Tel: 0300 200 3300

615 WEST WALES AREA (ABERYSTWYTH)

Customer Operations
Government Buildings
Ty Glas
Llanishen
Cardiff CF14 5ZA
Tel: 0300 200 3300

615 WEST WALES AREA (BRIDGEND)

Customer Operations
Government Buildings
Ty Glas
Llanishen
Cardiff CF14 5ZA
Tel: 0300 200 3300

615 WEST WALES AREA (CARMARTHEN)

Customer Operations
Government Buildings
Ty Glas
Llanishen
Cardiff CF14 5ZA
Tel: 0300 200 3300

700 WEST WALES AREA (COMPLIANCE)

Government Buildings
Ty Glas
Llanishen
Cardiff CF14 5FY

Tel: 0300 200 3410
(D)

615 **WEST WALES AREA
(EMPLOYERS)**

Customer Operations
Employer Team
BP 4009
Chillingham House
Benton Park View
Newcastle-upon-Tyne NE98
1ZZ
Tel: 0300 200 3200
Fax: 0191 285 4332/0300 052
3030

615 **WEST WALES AREA
(HAVERFORDWEST)**

Customer Operations
Government Buildings
Ty Glas
Llanishen
Cardiff CF14 5ZA
Tel: 0300 200 3300

615 **WEST WALES AREA
(LLANELLI)**

Customer Operations
Government Buildings
Ty Glas
Llanishen
Cardiff CF14 5ZA
Tel: 0300 200 3300

615 **WEST WALES AREA
(SERVICE)**

Customer Operations
Government Buildings
Ty Glas
Llanishen
Cardiff CF14 5ZA
Tel: 0300 200 3300

792 **WORCESTER & HEREFORD
AREA (COMPLIANCE)**

Aspect Gate
166 College Road
Harrow HA1 1BH
Tel: 0300 200 3410
(L) (D)

064 **WORCESTER & HEREFORD
AREA (EMPLOYERS)**

Customer Operations
Employer Team
BP 4009
Chillingham House
Benton Park View
Newcastle-upon-Tyne NE98
1ZZ
Tel: 0300 200 3200
Fax: 0191 285 4332/0300 052
3030

064 **WORCESTER & HEREFORD
AREA (EVESHAM)**

Customer Operations
City Centre House
30 Union Street
Birmingham B2 4AE
Tel: 0300 200 3300
Textphone: 0300 200 3319
From abroad: +44 135 535
9022

064 **WORCESTER & HEREFORD
AREA (HEREFORD)**

Customer Operations
City Centre House
30 Union Street
Birmingham B2 4AE
Tel: 0300 200 3300
Textphone: 0300 200 3319
From abroad: +44 135 535
9022

064 **WORCESTER & HEREFORD
AREA (LUDLOW)**

Customer Operations
City Centre House
30 Union Street
Birmingham B2 4AD
Tel: 0300 200 3300
Textphone: 0300 200 3319
From abroad: +44 135 535
9022

064 **WORCESTER & HEREFORD
AREA (REDDITCH)**

Customer Operations
City Centre House
30 Union Street

Birmingham B2 4AE
Tel: 0300 200 3300
Textphone: 0300 200 3319
From abroad: +44 135 535
9022

064 **WORCESTER & HEREFORD
AREA (SERVICE)**

Customer Operations
City Centre House
30 Union Street
Birmingham B2 4AE

Tel: 0300 200 3300
Textphone: 0300 200 3319
From abroad: +44 135 535
9022

893 **WREXHAM 2**
*(See Leics & Northants Area
(Claims). See* page 61.)

957 **YARMOUTH 2**
*(See Leics & Northants Area
(Claims). See* page 61.)

Employer Contact

Telephone contact numbers for employers are now dealt with at the Newcastle Office. This also provides support for new employers. Please direct queries to:
National Insurance Contributions and
Employers Office
HM Revenue and Customs
BX9 1BX
Tel: 0300 200 3200
Fax: 0300 052 3030

Paper forms P11D Expenses Payments and Benefits and all amendments should be sent to the following address:
HMRC NIC&EO
Room BP8002
Tynemouth House
Benton Park View
Longbenton Newcastle-upon-Tyne NE98 1ZZ

Where an S336 (expenses) claim is attached to the original paper P11D and submitted by an employer on behalf of an employee, the S336 claim and the P11D should be sent to: HMRC (NIC&EO), Room BP2101 at the above address.

Where an S336 claim is submitted *separately* on a form P87, form P810 or in letter format and is not attached to an original P11D, it should be clearly headed 'S336 claim' and have a copy of the P11D attached if possible (the P11D should be marked 'copy'). The S336 claim with the copy of the P11D attached should be sent to: Pay As You Earn and Self-Assessment, HM Revenue and Customs, BX9 1AS.

The Apprenticeship Levy: The Apprenticeship Levy, which is to be introduced in April 2017, will be a levy on UK employers to fund new apprenticeships. In England, control of apprenticeship funding will be put in the hands of employers through the Digital Apprenticeship Service. The levy will be charged at a rate of 0.5% of an employer's paybill. Each employer will receive an allowance of £15,000 to offset against their levy payment. For further information see www.gov.uk/government/publications/apprenticeship-levy/ap prenticeship-levy#further-advice.

The telephone contact numbers for individual employees now go to the Taxes Helpline: 0300 200 3300.

Self-employed individuals also have the option of using this line, or can telephone the new National Insurance for Self-Employed Helpline: 0300 200 3500.

HMRC now strongly recommend that employers register for its email alert service, so that they will receive reminders when the latest information is made available. The intention is to issue six email alerts a year – February, April, June, August, October and December. These will provide links to the latest Employer Bulletin. HMRC may also issue other messages throughout the year.

For full information about how to register, see www.hmrc.gov.uk/gds/payert i/forms-updates/forms-publications/register.htm.

Employer Contacts

Agent Contacts

Agent Priority Access

Agent Dedicated Line

HMRC Taxes Contact Centres can deal with taxpayer-specific queries from authorised agents. There is a dedicated line for agents and advisers which aims to provide them with a full and fast service.

The Contact Centre's Agent Dedicated Line is **0300 200 3311** and is available from 8am to 8pm from Monday to Friday and from 8am to 4pm on Saturday. HMRC recommend that agents use this number rather than the general number as when calling the Agent Dedicated Line agents and advisers will be given priority and have their calls answered quickly. They will be put through to a HMRC adviser who has at least 12 months' experience and, where necessary, the call will be transferred to technicians to ensure that wherever possible queries are answered on the first call.

HMRC stress that the Agent Dedicated Line is for authorised agents only and if they cannot verify that the caller is authorised to speak to HMRC on the client's behalf, they will not proceed with the call. HMRC also remind agents that they should not give the number of the Agent Dedicated Line to their clients.

There is a separate Agent Priority Line for Tax Credits: **0345 300 3943** (available 8.00 am to 8.00 pm, Monday to Friday and 8.00 am to 4.00 pm on Saturday).

There is also a Debt Management and Banking (DMB) agent-dedicated line for the sole use of agents with queries about DMB and provides priority service. Tel: **0300 200 3887** (available 8.00 am to 8.00 pm, Monday to Friday).

Agent Account Managers

HMRC has set up a UK-wide team of Agent Account Managers (AAMs) to help tax agents and advisers deal with the department more effectively.

Background

In 2007, following discussions with agent professional bodies, HMRC introduced AAMs as part of a pilot exercise. These AAMs acted as a single point of contact for a small number of agents in Edinburgh and Ipswich, providing help to resolve client-specific issues.

Following the success of the pilot, the AAM role has been successfully developed and tested. HMRC has now expanded the team to 40 officers based throughout the UK who will proactively help and support you in your interactions with HMRC.

AAMs provide an escalation route where agents have been unable to find an answer through the usual channels. Additionally, AAMs will be out and about to meet agents at national events and will be a direct point of contact for feedback on HMRC services.

Role of AAMs

AAMs can provide the following for tax agents and advisers:

- a streamlined process to resolve ongoing problems more quickly (the Agents' Issue Resolution Service);
- speakers for agent events and meetings; and
- co-ordination of HMRC Learning Together events.

Registering to use HMRC AAM services

Agents must register using an online form before they can make use of the services provided by the AAM team. You can also give HMRC permission to contact you about future events and products as they become available. Applicants will receive an automatic acknowledgement to their nominated email address and will be contacted within three working days if they need any more information. See www.gov.uk/guidance/agent-account-managers-in-h mrc.

Resolving client-specific problems

Should an agent encounter problems with any aspect of HMRC's service, there are escalation and complaints procedures in place for each business area. HMRC recommends that agents contact the office that they have been dealing with prior to contacting the AAM service in order to try and resolve the issue or to find out how to escalate it. To use the Agents' Issue Resolution Service, agents should complete an online form each time that they require AAM assistance. The form is accessed via the AAM pages of the HMRC website (o nline.hmrc.gov.uk/shortforms/form/AAMReg?dept-name=&sub-dept-name =&location=43&origin=http://www.hmrc.gov.uk). An email acknowledge ment is sent on receipt of the form and an AAM team member will contact the agent within three working days to discuss the next steps. HMRC also provides an opportunity to feedback on the Agents' Issue Resolution Service using an on line form available at https://online.hmrc.gov.uk/shortforms/form/AAM_FIR? dept.

De-registering from the AAM service

Agents who no longer wish to use the AAM service must de-register by completing an online form. This will remove the agent's details from the AAM database.

HMRC online services for agents

Using HMRC online services allows agents to carry out many tasks online, including registering a client's business for tax purposes, submitting tax returns, forms and declarations, making payments, requesting refunds, and viewing a client's accounts. Additionally, some forms and returns can now only be submitted online.

To register for online services, visit https://online.hmrc.gov.uk/registration/agent.

The following services are now covered: self assessment; corporation tax; PAYE/CIS; VAT online services; stamp taxes online; machine games duty; notification of vehicle arrivals; charities for agents online. Links explaining how to sign up for each one can be found at www.gov.uk/hmrc-online-services-for-agents.

Agent Authorisations

Agents are now encouraged to complete client authorisations online where possible. They need to have registered to use the service. The online service is faster and more secure than using paper forms.

To obtain an agent code for Self-Assessment or Corporation Tax, you must write to the Central Agent Maintainer Team (part of the Central Agent Authorisation Team) at National Insurance Contributions and Employer Office, HM Revenue and Customs, BX9 1AN on headed notepaper (if appropriate). You must provide your name, business name, address and telephone number along with details of the taxes you plan to deal with – for example Self-Assessment. You need a separate agent code for each tax. Further information on the process is here: www.gov.uk/guidance/client-authorisation-an-overview. Agents can contact the Online Services Helpdesk – 0300 200 3600 – for assistance. Opening hours are 8.00am–8.00pm, Monday to Friday, 8.00am–4.00pm, Saturday (closed Christmas Day, Boxing Day and New Year's Day). For customers who are deaf or hearing or speech-impaired: 0300 200 3603 (Textphone). If calling from abroad the number is: +44 161 930 8445.

Agents who cannot use the online agent authorisation service can ask clients to complete a paper form 64-8. One version of the form may be filled in online and then the completed version printed from www.gov.uk/government/publications/tax-agents-and-advisers-authorising-your-agent-64-8.

Alternatively, a printable copy of form 64-8 can be downloaded at www.gov.uk/government/uploads/system/uploads/attachment_data/file/489900/64-8.pdf.

The completed form should be sent to National Insurance Contributions and Employer Office, HM Revenue and Customs, BX9 1AN.

After completion, a paper form FBI 2 for authorisation to use the PAYE online or Construction Industry Scheme online services should be sent to: HM Revenue and Customs, Central Agent Authorisation Team, Benton Park View, Longbenton, Newcastle upon Tyne, NE98 1ZZ. HMRC aims to process these forms within ten working days.

Where charities appoint agents, the completed form 64-8 should be sent to: Charities, Savings and International 2, HM Revenue and Customs, BX9 1BU, *not* the address of the Central Agent Authorisation Team that is shown on the form. Where an agent is appointed as a nominee or the 'authorised official' (if the agent is already a 'manager' of the charity), it will also need to send a completed 'HMRC Change of Details Form' (ChV1) regarding the agent. For further information, see: www.hmrc.gov.uk/charities/guidance-notes/chapter2/fp-persons-test.htm.

NB: Agent authorisation for tax credits – form 64-8. Agent authorisations for self-assessment were previously accepted for tax credits. Now a client must complete a separate form 64-8 to authorise agents for tax credits if this was not specified on the original form. This cannot be done online.

VAT registrations and authorisations

HMRC warns that completion of a paper form 64-8 cannot be used to authorise an agent to act on their clients' behalf for VAT Online. If they want to do this, they must use the online authorisation process (see above) and agents must set up and register for the VAT for Agents online service.

Additionally, where a form 64-8 accompanies a VAT registration application (VAT 1) both forms must be sent to:
HM Revenue & Customs
VAT Registration Service
Crown House
Birch Street
Wolverhampton WV1 4JX

Non-resident agents and authorisations

From 1 April 2010, all paper 64-8 agent authorisation applications for non-resident agents and all applications from non-resident agents for Self Assessment agent codes (also known as agent reference numbers) – including changes to Self Assessment agent details – should now be sent, in writing, to:
The postal address is now:
Central Agent Maintainer Team
National Insurance Contributions and
Employer Office
HM Revenue and Customs BX9 1AN

The address for couriers remains:
HM Revenue & Customs
Central Agent Authorisation Team
Agent Maintainer
Benton Park View
Longbenton
Newcastle upon Tyne NE98 1ZZ

Working Together

Working Together is a partnership between HM Revenue and Customs (HMRC) and a wide range of main agent, and other representative bodies, which looks for ways to improve HMRC's operations for the benefit of tax agents, their clients and HMRC itself. The original members have now been joined by the following groups, which all actively participate:

- Association of International Accountants (AIA)
- Chartered Institute of Management Accountants (CIMA)
- Chartered Institute of Public Finance and Accountancy (CIPFA)
- Chartered Institute of Payroll Professionals (CIPP)
- Certified Public Accountants Association (CPAA)
- International Association of Bookkeepers (IAB)
- Institute of Chartered Accountants in Ireland (ICAI)
- Institute of Certified Bookkeepers (ICB)
- Independent Certified Practicing Accountants (ICPA)
- Institute of Financial Accountants (IFA)
- Society of Professional Accountants (SPA)
- Society of Trust and Estate Practitioners (STEP)
- VAT Practitioners Group (VPG)

The Issues Overview Group (IOG), formerly the Working Together Steering Group (WTSG), was set up to provide strategic direction. It holds quarterly telephone conferences, including one annual face-to-face meeting, to enable a free exchange of views on operational matters that are important both to HMRC and tax agents.

The IOG is made up of senior representatives from HMRC and the six main professional bodies:

- Chartered Institute of Taxation (CIOT)
- Institute of Chartered Accountants of Scotland (ICAS)
- Institute of Chartered Accountants in England and Wales (ICAEW)
- Association of Taxation Technicians (ATT)
- Association of Accounting Technicians (AAT)
- Association of Chartered Certified Accountants (ACCA)

The Working Together Team (WTT)

The WTT maintains an issues register providing details of all widespread issues. These issues are prioritised by the Professional Bodies (PBs) on the IOG and the highest priority ones are monitored by the Joint Initiative Steering Group (JISG).

The key aims of the IOG are to:

- focus on systemic issues where HMRC procedures and service affect tax agents and their clients;
- deal with new issues of national importance when they arise;
- agree key priorities and check on their progress;

- receive information on reviews or projects being carried out by HMRC;
- make sure agents' views are passed to consultation groups; and to
- identify opportunities to work together to improve HMRC's service to agents and their clients.

The publication 'Working Together' has been discontinued and items of concern to practitioners are now incorporated into Agent Update, available at www.gov.uk/government/collections/agent-update.

HMRC have recently added new help and support for tax agents and advisers with the programme of Agent Talking Points, weekly online digital meetings designed specifically for tax agents and advisors, which sit alongside its regular monthly Working Together online meetings with agents.

They are short online sessions, usually 45 minutes to an hour, focusing on topics agents have highlighted as of interest or on emerging issues jointly identified by agents and HMRC that may have widespread impact.

Talking Points sessions offer agents the opportunity to ask questions to subject matter experts from HMRC, across a range of different topics. Registration is quick and easy, but should be done at least five minutes before the start of a digital meeting. For further information see www.gov.uk/government/news/w ebinars-e-learning-and-videos-if-youre-a-tax-agent-or-adviser.

Comments on the WT programme can be sent direct to the HMRC WT team or the relevant professional body representative (contact details below). If contacting your professional body, please make it clear that your comment is about WT.

Contacts

Organisation	Contact Name	Email Address
Editor	Andria Barber	andria.barber@hmrc.gsi.gov.uk
CIOT	Nigel Clarke	wt@tax.org.uk
ICAEW	Caroline Miskin	Caroline.miskin@icaew.com
ACCA	Jason Piper	jason.piper@accaglobal.com
ICAS	Charlotte Barbour	tax@icas.org.uk
ATT	Jon Stride	wt@att.org.uk
AAT	Jeremy Nottingham	wt@aat.org.uk
AIA	Tim Pinkney	workingtogether@aiaworldwide.com
IAB	Kelly Lant	kellyl@aib.org.uk
VATPG	Ruth Corkin	ruth.corkin@uk.gt.com
CIPP	(no name)	policy@cipp.org.uk
ICPA	Tony Margaritelli	admin@icpa.org.uk

Further general information is available at www.gov.uk/government/publicati ons/working-together/working-together-and-local-working-together-meetings

Working Together – Regional Groups

Across the UK there are ten regional Working Together groups: London, South West, South East, East and East Midlands, West Midlands, North West, North

East, Wales, Scotland and Northern Ireland. There will be a minimum of ten online meetings a year hosted by the regional groups. All meetings have formal agendas and regular feedback is provided to group members on issues raised.

Each regional group has a dedicated named contact, backed by a support network, ensuring agents always have access to a Specialist Agent Manager (SAM).

Every regional group will also have access to a digital forum (currently in design) so agents can self-serve information when it's convenient for them, and for HMRC to post updates on Working Together/Issue Resolution, providing prompt information and faster resolution. Online meetings will give agents unprecedented access to Subject Matter Experts and HMRC business owners and leaders, ensuring communications are consistent and UK-wide.

Working Together in a Digital Age

The former system of local groups has been superseded by a new digital approach. Working Together groups hold online meetings to give tax agents the opportunity to raise and discuss issues with HMRC, and to hear messages from the department. Any agent is welcome to join these WT online meetings. Some agents in regional groups will represent one of the main representative bodies, or other agent organisations. Agents attending the online meetings are asked, where appropriate, to bring discussion items from colleagues and feed back to them after each meeting. If you are not yet involved in Digital WT and would like to be, please contact your PB, via the email link in the above listing.

Future Relationships

HMRC is continuing to update its 'agent strategy' following a review on how it would work with agents in the future.

According to the HMRC Agents' Blog, (https://taxagents.blog.gov.uk/2015/03/06/building-the-future-for-tax-agents) and a Q&A article in the 4 March 2015 Tax Journal by HMRC's Director General for Business Tax, Jim Harra, the plans for future changes include plans to incentivise agents:

HMRC plans to launch new personalised digital services for our customers, which means that it will be much easier and more intuitive for them to interact with the tax system. 'Your tax account', which already has over two million users, is a step towards that. (See below for more on Personal Tax Accounts.)

It believes that taxpayers will be looking to agents to either deliver them a lower-cost service or, more likely, a service which adds value to the one they get now. They are likely to look to agents to help them to deal with the more complex issues and actively help them to stay on the right side of compliance.

HMRC wants to provide a better opportunity for agents to manage upfront the compliance risks their clients might present, because this is better for the client, better for HMRC and better for the agent, which can market this service.

HMRC's research shows that while about 70% of small and mid-sized businesses currently use a tax agent; small and mid-sized business non-compliance still represents an estimated 44% of the £34bn UK tax gap – the difference between the tax due, and the amount actually received.

Incentivising change

It therefore wants to be able to differentiate between the agents that offer value-added services and those that don't, and to incentivise all agents to provide these services – and adhere to high standards. Part of this incentive would be making sure that those agents that provide more get the credit for doing so – whether that involves being able to take on a wider range of functions for their clients via our online services, or by receiving fewer low value interventions from HMRC. Exactly how we work with agents will vary, though, according to their needs, their compliance history and the value they add to the administration of the tax system.

New digital plans

The future is clearly digital. HMRC plan that the role of the tax agent will be built-in when rolling out new digital services, because they will be as central to the tax system of tomorrow as they are to the tax system today. What was formerly 'Agent online self-serve' (AOSS), now renamed Agent Services (AS), is an online service aimed principally at professional tax agents, which will eventually replace the existing online service and act as the foundation stone for a range of expanded and improved services for agents in the future. The project has four new key priorities for 2016/17.

These are:

- On-boarding – to enable agents to access services and features contained in the Personal and the Business Tax account using third party software which will make them able to see and do what their clients are able to do through their tax account.
- Subscription – a process that will allow HMRC to collect data about a tax agency as part of the Agent Strategy.
- Authorisation – to enhance the existing online agent authorisation (OAA) service.
- Inbound Secure Messaging – work to understand what information agents want to send to HMRC and explore the digital solutions that can cater for this requirement.

The Government is committed to building a transparent and accessible tax system fit for the digital age and thereby reducing burdens for taxpayers. In December 2015 it launched the Making Tax Digital Roadmap setting out how this would be achieved, to make HMRC into one of the most digitally-advanced tax administrations in the world by 2020.

It then published six consultation documents, each focusing on specific customer groups or elements of the Making Tax Digital reforms. The consultation period opened on 15 August 2016 and was due to close on 7 November 2016.

The areas covered included:

- bringing business tax into the digital age;
- simplifying tax for unincorporated businesses;
- simplified cash basis for unincorporated property businesses;
- voluntary pay as you go;
- tax administration; and
- transforming the tax system through the better use of information.

There was also a special document offering 'an overview for small businesses, the self-employed and smaller landlords' providing an easier way to respond to the Making Tax Digital consultations, specifically aimed at small businesses and landlords.

Full details of all the consultations can be found at www.gov.uk/government/collections/making-tax-digital-consultations.

Personal Tax Accounts

Personal Tax Accounts were made available to all taxpayers from August 2016. Ruth Owen, Director General of Customer Service, HMRC said: 'This new service puts customers in control of their tax affairs allowing them to claim any money owing to them immediately'.

The online tax refund service means that tax that has been overpaid will be returned directly to their bank account within three to five days rather than the two weeks it would typically take for a cheque to be issued, banked and cleared.

The Personal Tax Account covers over 34 quick and easy services which would have previously involved a letter or phone call to HMRC. These include being able to: view and update personal details; see how their tax is calculated; check the expected level of their state pension; and see tax credits payments and report changes in circumstances.

Webchat is also available to support customers who need help while accessing their online tax account. Further information is available at www.gov.uk/government/news/faster-easier-tax-repayments-at-the-heart-of-the-personal-tax-account.

Enforcing standards

HM Revenue and Customs has issued a standard for agents, which is intended to ensure that there is a minimum standard for all agents to comply with – in particular, those unaffiliated to any professional body. This supplements the Professional Conduct in Relation to Taxation set by the largest professional bodies, which it recognises is already being met by many tax agents and advisers.

The standard lays down what it expects in terms of integrity, competence and care and professional behaviour (see below). See also www.gov.uk/government/publications/hmrc-the-standard-for-agents.

Working Together

Integrity

HMRC expect agents to be straightforward and honest with them, for example, they should:

- disclose all relevant information; and
- don't imply that they are regulated for tax by HMRC.

Professional competence and due care

HMRC expect agents to:

- keep correct and up-to-date knowledge of the areas of tax that they deal with;
- work to prevent errors in their clients' tax calculations or claims;
- advise their client to take steps to set matters right where they find errors in their client's tax affairs; and
- keep online access credentials safe from unauthorised use at all times.

Professional behaviour

HMRC expect agents to:

- comply fully with tax law and regulations;
- ensure their own tax affairs are correct and up-to-date;
- deal courteously and professionally with HMRC staff; and
- consider the risk to reputation of tax agents, of any arrangements that they advise a client about – for example, tax planning schemes.

Secure communications

HMRC aims to provide a secure electronic communication service with HMRC as part of AS, although this function will not initially be part of the service. Initially, it will concentrate on providing access to employer PAYE accounts and will then bring in a new digital authorisation and registration service and a personalised agents' homepage. These services will be released in stages, once they have been fully tested and feedback from agents has been fed into the solution every step of the way.

The fact that it initially introduced AOSS to deal with PAYE is based on agents' feedback that this is a priority area for them – further reflecting the long association with agents and their professional bodies.

Views from tax professionals are invited.

Website transition

HMRC's web guidance and tools have moved to the cross-government www .gov.uk website, where customers can access all government information and services in one place. The website is intended to provide a clearer, faster way for people to find what they need.

HMRC has provided information to assist agents in finding material which was available on the former HMRC website but may not have been transferred across to the new government site. It can be found at p 14 of Agent Update 52 (www.gov.uk/government/uploads/system/uploads/attachment_data/file/502266/5178_Agent_Update___WT_52_accessible.pdf).

Joint Initiative on Service Delivery

The latest edition of Agent Update can be found at www.gov.uk/government/publications/agent-update. HMRC send out email reminders when future editions of Agent Update are published.

Tax Repayment Office

HMRC advises that customers who may be due a repayment of income tax on their PAYE or self-assessment should contact their usual tax office.

However, where the taxpayer does not have another tax office, all claims to repayment of tax on investment income (such as bank and building society interest) and completed forms R40 should be sent to the remaining repayment claims office.

Leics & Northants (Claims)
Saxon House
1 Causeway Lane
Leicester LE1 4AA
Tel: 0300 200 3313

(Line open Monday to Friday 8.30am-5pm except for public holidays)

Tax Office Tracer

Tax Offices are listed below in numerical order so that the office name may be traced from the official number. Please refer to the main entry for details. The letter C or S next to each office indicates that payments of tax are normally sent to the main Accounts Office at Cumbernauld (C) or Shipley (S).

NB: This information is historic but has been retained here due to reader requests.

005	Liverpool LBS	C
034	Bristol & N Somerset (Bath)	S
034	Bristol & N Somerset (Employers)	S
034	Bristol & N Somerset (Service)	S
034	Bristol & N Somerset (Weston-Super-Mare)	S
036	Bristol & N Somerset (Compliance)	S
049	Bristol & N Somerset (Bournemouth)	S
054	West Midlands LBS (CT)	C
064	Worcester & Hereford (Employers)	C
064	Worcester & Hereford (Evesham)	C
064	Worcester & Hereford (Hereford)	C
064	Worcester & Hereford (Ludlow)	C
064	Worcester & Hereford (Redditch)	C
064	Worcester & Hereford (Service)	C
065	NW Lancs (Blackpool)	C
065	NW Lancashire (Chorley)	C
065	NW Lancashire (Employers)	
065	NW Lancashire (Lancaster)	C
065	NW Lancashire (St Annes)	C
065	N W Lancashire (Service)	C
066	Glos & N Wilts (Compliance)	C
068	Birmingham Solihull (Employers)	C
068	Birmingham Solihull (Service)	C
070	Devon (Barnstaple)	S
070	Devon (Bideford)	S
070	Devon (Employers)	S
070	Devon (Harrow SA)	S
070	Devon (Newton Abbot)	S
070	Devon (Service)	S
070	Devon (Torquay)	S
071	Devon (Compliance)	S
072	W Yorks & Craven (Employers)	C
072	W Yorks & Craven (Halifax)	C
072	W Yorks & Craven (Huddersfield)	C
072	W Yorks & Craven (Keighley)	C
072	W Yorks & Craven (Service)	C
072	W Yorks & Craven (Skipton)	C
073	W Yorks & Craven(Employers)	C

073	W Yorks & Craven (Service)	C
075	South Wales (Oxford)	S
077	Sefton (Compliance)	C
080	Manchester (Employers)	C
080	Manchester (Service)	C
083	Sefton (Employers)	C
083	Sefton (Service)	C
084	East Herts West Essex (Compliance)	C
095	East Lancs (Compliance)	C
100	W Yorks & Craven (Compliance)	C
106	East Lancs (Accrington)	C
106	East Lancs (Burnley)	C
106	East Lancs (Employers)	C
106	East Lancs (Pendle)	C
106	East Lancs (Rochdale)	C
106	East Lancs (Service)	C
110	Leics & Northants (Compliance)	C
115	North Yorks (London SA)	C
120	Northeast Met (Employers)	S
120	Northeast Met (LP10)	S
120	Northeast Met (LP34)	S
120	Northeast Met (Service)	S
120	Northeast Met (Washington)	S
126	Cambridgeshire (Cambridge)	C
126	Cambridgeshire (Employers)	C
126	Cambridgeshire (Huntingdon)	C
126	Cambridgeshire (Peterborough)	C
126	Cambridgeshire (Service)	C
133	Cambridge (Compliance)	C
190	Warwickshire Coventry (Employers)	C
190	Warwickshire Coventry (Leamington)	C
190	Warwickshire Coventry (Nuneaton)	C
190	Warwickshire Coventry (Rugby)	C
190	Warwickshire Coventry (Service)	C
190	Warwickshire Coventry (Stratford-on-Avon)	C
193	W London (Ealing Broadway Tax Shop)	S
193	W London (Service)	S
195	Warwickshire Coventry (Compliance)	C
201	South London (CT only)	S
204	South Wales (Compliance)	S
209	North London (Edgware)	S
209	North London (Enfield)	S
209	North London (Finchley)	S
209	North London (Hendon)	S
209	North London (Hornsley)	S
209	North London (Service)	S
214	Glos & N Wilts (Cheltenham)	C
214	Glos & N Wilts (Chippenham)	C
214	Glos & N Wilts (Employers)	C
214	Glos & N Wilts (Service)	C
214	Glos & N Wilts (Stroud)	C
214	Glos & N Wilts (Swindon)	C
222	SE London (Service)	S
224	SE London (Compliance)	S
226	North London (Compliance)	S

245	Suffolk & N Essex (Bury St Edmunds)	C
245	Suffolk & N Essex (Clacton)	C
245	Suffolk & N Essex (Colchester)	C
245	Suffolk & N Essex (Employers)	C
245	Suffolk & N Essex (Service)	C
245	Suffolk & N Essex (Sudbury)	C
245	Suffolk & N Essex (Witham)	C
261	Public Departments (London)	
267	Leics & Northants (Employers)	C
267	Leics & Northants (Kettering)	C
267	Leics & Northants (Melton Mowbray)	C
267	Leics & Northants (Northampton)	C
267	Leics & Northants (Service)	C
267	Leics & Northants (Wellingborough)	C
268	London Finance Office for the Large Business Service	
281	West London (Compliance)	S
281	West London (Ealing Broadway) (Compliance)	S
294	Leeds LBS (CT)	C
301	Central London (Service)	S
305	City of London (Service)	S
321	East Herts West Essex (Employers)	C
321	East Herts West Essex (Harlow)	C
321	East Herts West Essex (Hatfield)	C

321	East Herts West Essex (Hertford)	C
321	East Herts West Essex (Hitchin)	C
321	East Herts West Essex (Service)	C
333	Sussex (Compliance)	S
334	Sussex (Chichester)	S
334	Sussex (Crawley)	S
334	Sussex (Employers)	S
334	Sussex (Hastings)	S
334	Sussex (Horsham)	S
334	Sussex (Lewes)	S
334	Sussex (Service)	S
334	Sussex (Worthing)	S
336	Humber (Compliance)	C
346	Suffolk & N Essex (Compliance)	C
356	Cumbria (Compliance)	C
362	Oxon & Bucks (Aylesbury)	C
362	Oxon & Bucks (Banbury)	C
362	Oxon & Bucks (Employers)	C
362	Oxon & Bucks (High Wycombe)	C
362	Oxon & Bucks (Milton Keynes)	C
362	Oxon & Bucks (Oxford)	C
362	Oxon & Bucks (Service)	C
373	Lincolnshire (Compliance)	C
388	Central Yorkshire (Compliance)	C
391	Humber (Employers)	C
391	Humber (Goole)	C
391	Humber (Grimsby)	C
391	Humber (Scunthorpe)	C
391	Humber (Service)	C
397	Manchester LBS (CT)	C
398	W Yorks & Craven (PTU)	S

402	Oxon & Bucks (Compliance)	C
406	Tees Valley (Bishop Auckland)	C
406	Tees Valley (Darlington)	C
406	Tees Valley (Employers)	C
406	Tees Valley (Service)	C
417	Tees Valley (Compliance)	C
419	Beds & West Herts (Bedford Chail)	C
419	Beds & West Herts (Bedford Port)	C
419	Beds & West Herts (Employers)	C
419	Beds & West Herts (Hemel Hempstead)	C
419	Beds & West Herts (Luton King)	C
419	Beds & West Herts (Luton Raglan)	C
419	Beds & West Herts (St Albans)	C
419	Beds & West Herts (Service)	C
419	Beds & West Herts (Watford)	C
421	Manchester (Compliance)	C
423	Merseyside (Compliance)	C
428	Merseyside (Employers)	C
428	Merseyside (Service)	C
428	Merseyside (Southport)	C
428	Merseyside (Wirral)	C
438	Beds & West Herts (Compliance)	C
449	NW Lancs (Compliance)	C
450	Birmingham Solihull (Compliance)	C
455	NW London (Harrow Compliance)	S
455	NW London (Wembley Compliance)	S
461	NW London (Euston Square)	S
461	NW London (Ruislip)	S
461	NW London (Service)	S
461	NW London (Wembley IREC)	S
465	Wear & S Tyne (Durham)	C
465	Wear & S Tyne (Employers)	C
465	Wear & S Tyne (Service)	C
470	Cornwall & Plymouth (Employers)	S
470	Cornwall & Plymouth (Launceston)	S
470	Cornwall & Plymouth (Penzance)	S
470	Cornwall & Plymouth (Redruth)	S
470	Cornwall & Plymouth (St Austell)	S
470	Cornwall & Plymouth (Service)	S
470	Cornwall & Plymouth (Truro)	S
474	Cornwall & Plymouth (Compliance)	S
475	Lincolnshire (Boston)	C
475	Lincolnshire (Employers)	C
475	Lincolnshire (Gainsborough)	C
475	Lincolnshire (Grantham)	C
475	Lincolnshire (Louth)	C
475	Lincolnshire (Retford)	C
475	Lincolnshire (Service)	C
475	Lincolnshire (Spalding)	C
484	Nottingham – IR Trusts	C
486	E Hampshire & Wight (Compliance)	S
503	Dorset & S Wilts (Dorchester)	S
503	Dorset & S Wilts (Employers)	S
503	Dorset & S Wilts (Salisbury)	S

503	Dorset & S Wilts (Service)	S
504	Northumbria (Alnwick)	C
504	Northumbria (Employers)	C
504	Northumbria (Hexham)	C
504	Northumbria (London SA)	C
504	Northumbria (Morpeth)	C
504	Northumbria (Newcastle)	C
504	Northumbria (Service)	C
507	Notts & Derbyshire (Alfreton)	C
507	Notts & Derbyshire (Derby)	C
507	Notts & Derbyshire (Employers)	C
507	Notts & Derbyshire (Mansfield)	C
507	Notts & Derbyshire (Newark)	C
507	Notts & Derbyshire (Service)	C
513	Northumbria (Compliance)	C
529	Norfolk (Compliance)	C
531	Norfolk (Dereham)	C
531	Norfolk (Employers)	C
531	Norfolk (Great Yarmouth)	C
531	Norfolk (Kings Lynn)	C
531	Norfolk (London SA)	C
531	Norfolk (Service)	C
532	Notts and Derbyshire (Compliance)	C
539	Lisburn (Compliance)	S
549	Peterborough LBS (CT)	C
567	Central Yorkshire (Dewsbury)	C
567	Central Yorkshire (Employers)	C
567	Central Yorkshire (Pontefract)	C
567	Central Yorkshire (Service)	C
567	Central Yorkshire (Wakefield)	C
570	Cambridgeshire (Compliance)	C
571	Westminster (Compliance)	S
572	Nottingham LBS (CT)	C
577	Kent (Ashford)	S
577	Kent (Employers)	S
577	Kent (Gravesend)	S
577	Kent (London SA)	S
577	Kent (Margate)	S
577	Kent (Medway)	S
577	Kent (Service)	S
577	Kent (Tonbridge)	S
577	Kent (Tunbridge Wells)	S
578	Dorset & S Wilts (Compliance)	S
579	Kent (Compliance)	S
581	E Hampshire & Wight (Employers)	S
581	E Hampshire & Wight (Isle of Wight)	S
581	E Hampshire & Wight (Portsmouth Maritime)	S
581	E Hampshire & Wight (Service)	S
582	E Cheshire & S Lancs (Ashton-under-Lyne)	C
582	E Cheshire & S Lancs (Employers)	C
582	E Cheshire & S Lancs (Macclesfield)	C
582	E Cheshire & S Lancs (Oldham Pennine)	C
582	E Cheshire & S Lancs (Service)	C
585	North Yorks (Bridlington)	C
585	North Yorks (Employers)	C
585	North Yorks (Harrogate)	C
585	North Yorks (Ripon)	C
585	North Yorks (Scarborough)	C

585	North Yorks (Service)	C
586	Staffordshire (Burton-on-Trent)	C
586	Staffordshire (Cannock)	C
586	Staffordshire (Employers)	C
586	Staffordshire (Leek)	C
586	Staffordshire (Service)	C
586	Staffordshire (Stafford)	C
592	Berkshire (Newbury)	S
592	Berkshire (Service)	S
592	Berkshire (Slough)	S
599	SW London (Kingston-upon-Thames)	S
599	SW London (Service)	S
610	Berkshire (Compliance)	S
615	West Wales (Aberystwyth)	S
615	West Wales (Bridgend)	S
615	West Wales (Carmarthen)	S
615	West Wales (Employers)	S
615	West Wales (Haverfordwest)	S
615	West Wales (Llanelli)	S
615	West Wales (Service)	S
623	Central London (Compliance)	S
626	Wear & S Tyne (Compliance)	C
653	Midlands West (Employers)	C
653	Midlands West (Service)	C
660	Bristol LBS	S
662	South Essex (Basildon)	C
662	South Essex (Chelmsford)	C
662	South Essex (Employers)	C
662	South Essex (Grays)	C
662	South Essex (London SA)	C
662	South Essex (Service)	C
663	West Hampshire (Andover)	S
663	West Hampshire (Employers)	S
663	West Hampshire (Service)	S
663	West Hampshire (Winchester)	S
664	West Hampshire (Compliance)	S
665	South Essex (Compliance)	C
671	NW Midlands & Shrops (Employers)	C
671	NW Midlands & Shrops (Oswestry)	C
671	NW Midlands & Shrops (Service)	C
671	NW Midlands & Shrops (Telford)	C
671	NW Midlands & Shrops (Walsall)	C
673	South Yorkshire (Barnsley)	C
673	South Yorkshire (Chesterfield)	C
673	South Yorkshire (Doncaster)	C
673	South Yorkshire (Employers)	C
673	South Yorkshire (Service)	C
673	South Yorkshire (Sheffield)	C
680	City of London (Compliance)	S
682	E Cheshire & S Lancs (Compliance)	C
686	Berkshire (London SA)	S
687	Staffordshire (Compliance)	C
693	Midlands West (Compliance)	C
700	West Wales (Compliance)	S
	Newcastle LBS	
705	Somerset (Compliance)	S

709	W Lancs & W Cheshire (Chester)	C
709	W Lancs & W Cheshire (Crewe)	C
709	W Lancs & W Cheshire (Employers)	C
709	W Lancs & W Cheshire (Leigh)	C
709	W Lancs & W Cheshire (Northwich)	C
709	W Lancs & W Cheshire (St Helens)	C
709	W Lancs & W Cheshire (Service)	C
709	W Lancs & W Cheshire (Warrington)	C
709	W Lancs & W Cheshire (Widnes)	C
709	W Lancs & W Cheshire (Wigan)	C
712	Truro – IR Trusts	S
714	South West London (Compliance)	S
717	East London (Ilford)	S
717	East London (Romford)	S
717	East London (Service)	S
717	East London (Stratford)	S
717	East London (Walthamstow)	S
725	South Yorks (Compliance)	C
733	East London (CT)	S
738	Surrey & N Hants (Compliance)	S
750	W Lancs & W Cheshire (Compliance)	C
765	Surrey & N Hants (Basingstoke)	S
765	Surrey & N Hants (Employers)	S
765	Surrey & N Hants (Epsom)	S
765	Surrey & N Hants (Service)	S
765	Surrey & N Hants (Staines)	S
765	Surrey & N Hants (Walton-on-Thames)	S
778	NW Midlands & Shrops (Compliance)	C
783	Cumbria (Carlisle)	C
783	Cumbria (Employers)	C
783	Cumbria (Furness)	C
783	Cumbria (Kendal)	C
783	Cumbria (Penrith)	C
783	Cumbria (Service)	C
791	N Yorks (Compliance)	C
792	Worcester & Hereford (Compliance)	C
793	North Wales (Compliance)	S
794	Somerset (Bridgwater)	S
794	Somerset (Employers)	S
794	Somerset (Frome)	S
794	Somerset (Service)	S
794	Somerset (Wells)	S
794	Somerset (Yeovil)	S
795	Scotland North (Compliance)	C
799	Scotland West (Ayr)	C
799	Scotland West (Dumbarton)	C
799	Scotland West (Dumfries)	C
799	Scotland West (Dunoon)	C
799	Scotland West (Greenock)	C
799	Scotland West (Irvine)	C
799	Scotland West (Rothesay)	C
799	Scotland West (Service)	C
801	Scotland South (Falkirk)	C
801	Scotland South (Galashiels)	C
801	Scotland South (Hawick)	C
801	Scotland South (Service)	C
801	Scotland South (Stirling)	C
808	Scotland West (Corporation Tax)	C

Tax Office Tracer

809	Scotland South (Compliance)	C
817	Scotland Central (Compliance)	C
820	Scotland West (Compliance)	C
825	Scotland East (Compliance)	C
834	Edinburgh LBS (CT)	C
837	Scotland East (Dunfermline)	C
837	Scotland East (Kirkcaldy)	C
837	Scotland East (Perth)	C
837	Scotland East (Service)	C
840	Sefton (London SA)	C
842	Cornwall & Plymouth (Redhill/London SA)	S
843	Lothians (Compliance)	S
846	Lothians (Claims)	S
846	Lothians (Employers)	S
846	Lothians (Glenrothes)	S
846	Lothians (Grayfield)	S
846	Lothians (Pentland)	S
846	Lothians (Service)	S
852	Scotland Central (Coatbridge)	C
852	Scotland Central (Hamilton)	C
852	Scotland Central (Motherwell)	C
852	Scotland Central (Paisley)	C
852	Scotland Central (Service)	C
854	Glasgow LBS (CT)	C
856	Leics & Northants (Claims)	C
864	Leics & Northants (Croydon SA)	C
865	Scotland East (London SA)	C
875	Centre 1 (Service)	C
880	Northeast Metropolitan (Compliance)	C
892	Leics & Northants (IBTO)	C
900	Centre for Revenue Intelligence	
905	Northeast Met (Film Unit)	S
914	North Wales (Bangor)	S
914	North Wales (Colwyn Bay)	S
914	North Wales (Employers)	S
914	North Wales (Porthmadog)	S
914	North Wales (Rhyl)	S
914	North Wales (Service)	S
914	North Wales (Welshpool)	S
916	N Ireland (Ballymena)	S
916	N Ireland (Coleraine)	S
916	N Ireland (Employers)	S
916	N Ireland (Enniskillen)	S
916	N Ireland (London SA)	S
916	N Ireland (Newry)	S
916	N Ireland (Service)	S
923	Chapel Wharf (Compliance)	S
925	Greater Belfast (Employers)	S
925	Greater Belfast (Service)	S
933	Greater Belfast (Compliance)	S
940	Public Department 1	S
948	South Wales (Brecon)	S
948	South Wales (Cardiff 1)	S
948	South Wales (Employers)	S
948	South Wales (Merthyr Tydfil)	S
948	South Wales (Newport)	S
948	South Wales (Pontypool)	S
948	South Wales (Pontypridd)	S
948	South Wales (Service)	S

951	Chapel Wharf (Employers)	S
951	Chapel Wharf (Service)	S
953	Lisburn (Employers)	S
953	Lisburn (Service)	S
961	Centre 1 (Employers)	C
961	Centre 1 (Service)	C
965	Sefton (Claims)	
974	Greater Belfast (Claims)	
975	Holyrood	C
976	Centre 1 (Compliance)	C

978	Edinburgh – IR Trusts	C
985	Scotland North (Buckie)	C
985	Scotland North (Inverness)	C
985	Scotland North (Peterhead)	C
985	Scotland North (Service)	C
985	Scotland North (Wick)	C
987	N Ireland (Compliance)	S
992	Sefton (Service)	S

Recovery (Tax Collection) Offices

Since 1 April 2011, companies and organisations have had to submit their Company Tax Returns and pay all Corporation Tax and related payments electronically. Full details of payment methods can be found at: www.gov.uk/pay-corporation-tax/overview. Cheque payments for Corporation Tax should no longer be sent to HMRC.

On any occasion when, exceptionally, payment is made by cheque after March 2011, the funds will be treated as being received by HMRC on the date when cleared funds reach HMRC's bank account – not the date when HMRC receives the cheque.

For further information about making Corporation Tax payments please see: www.gov.uk/pay-corporation-tax.

If paying by post:

- make the cheque payable to 'HM Revenue & Customs only' and write the Corporation Tax reference after 'HM Revenue & Customs only';
- detach the HMRC payslip for the relevant accounting period and send it with the cheque to HMRC using the pre-addressed envelope or the address below; and
- do not fold the payslip or cheque and do not fasten them together in any way.

If sending a payment to HMRC without an HMRC pre-addressed envelope send your payment to:
HM Revenue and Customs
Bradford BD98 1YY

If paying HMRC by post and requiring a receipt, you will need to include a separate request by letter with the payment. HMRC cannot identify any instructions written on payslips, as they are processed automatically.

HMRC encourages customers to pay electronically and thus avoid the expense of the stamp, potential expense of a penalty and stress worrying whether your payment will reach HMRC in time. Further details are available at www.gov.uk/pay-paye-tax or by telephoning the Payment Enquiry Helpline on 0300 200 3401 for advice on the correct electronic payment method. The Helpline is open 8.00 am to 8.00 pm Monday to Friday, and 8.00am–4.00pm on Saturday.

An Enforcement & Compliance, Debt Management & Banking (DMB) agent-dedicated helpline providing priority service for the sole use of agents with queries about DMB is available. Tel: 0300 200 3887 (8.00 am to 8.00 pm, Monday to Friday).

Recovery visits

HM Revenue & Customs (HMRC) visits a small number of customers who have not paid their tax or arranged to repay overpayments of tax credits, in order to collect the debt. Visits are undertaken by Debt Management and Banking's Field Force Collectors and can take place at a customer's home or business premises.

If a debt is not paid, advance warning is always provided to a customer that a visit may take place. To provide a safeguard against bogus callers in these situations, HMRC has introduced a new Field Force Verification Helpline, so that a customer can easily check whether or not a caller on their doorstep claiming to be from HMRC is, in fact, genuine. To access the Helpline, customers should follow these simple steps:

- ask to see the Collector's photo ID;
- make a note of the ID number on the photo ID;
- call 0300 200 3862 and provide HMRC with the ID number you've noted.

HMRC will then be able to confirm to you whether or not your caller is a genuine HMRC Collector.

HMRC may also, in some cases, refer a debt to a private debt collection agency and has advised that it will be using the following agencies to pursue some debts on its behalf (list as at 4 October 2016):

- Advantis Credit Ltd;
- Akinika Debt Recovery Ltd;
- Apex Credit Management Ltd;
- Bluestone Credit Management Ltd;
- Commercial Collection Services Ltd (trading as CCS Collect);
- Drydensfairfax Solicitors;
- 1st Locate (trading as LCS);
- Fredrickson International Ltd;
- Moorcroft;
- Past Due Credit Solutions (PDCS);
- Rossendales Ltd; and
- Walker Love.

HMRC may also ask a debt collection agency to visit the taxpayer's home to collect the debt in person.

The agent's identity can be checked by looking up their name on the Certified Bailiff Register at certificatedbailiffs.justice.gov.uk/CertificatedBailiffs/.

To tell HMRC about a change (such as a new address) you should include a separate letter with payment if paying by post, or write separately to the following address, if payment has been made electronically: HM Revenue and Customs, St Mungo's Road, Cumbernauld, Glasgow G67 1YZ.

ACCOUNTS OFFICES

CUMBERNAULD

St Mungo's Road
Town Centre
Cumbernauld
Glasgow G67 1YZ
Corporation Tax Unit: 0300 200 3410
Group Payments: 03000 583 947
Self-Assessment and PAYE: 0300 200
3401
DX: 550575 Cumbernauld 3
(D)

NEWCASTLE

Benton Park Road
Newcastle upon Tyne NE98 1ZZ
Tel: 0300 200 3200
Fax: 0191 285 4332/0300 052 3030

Recovery Offices

Specialist Tax Functions

Contact details for the offices which deal with various taxes and administrative functions are given on the following pages in alphabetical order.

(D) = Disabled facilities: (L) = Letterbox

ANTI AVOIDANCE GROUP (INTELLIGENCE)

Bush House
Southwest Wing
The Strand
London WC2B 4RD
Tel: 0300 058 8993
email: aag@hmrc.gov.uk
Post to:

HM Revenue and Customs
CTIAA Intelligence SO528 PO Box 194
Bootle L69 9AA

BUSINESS SUPPORT TEAMS

Business Support teams were previously organised on a regional basis. However, all telephone calls should now be made to 0300 123 1083.

CAPITAL GAINS TAX

Capital Gains Tax enquiries for individuals, employees and self-employed:

HM Revenue and Customs
Capital Gains Tax Queries BX9 1AS
Tel: (Taxes Helpline): 0300 200 3300

CENTRE FOR NON-RESIDENTS

The Centre for Non-Residents has been disbanded. Please see HMRC Residency below.

CHARITIES

(England Wales, N Ireland)
Charities, Savings and International 2
HM Revenue and Customs BX9 1BU
Tel: (helpline and form requests): 0300 123 1073
(Gift Aid enquiries also on this line)
(Scotland)

(The Office of the Scottish Charity Regulator has assumed responsibility for recognising all charities operating in Scotland (see Charities Sector at page 145))

CHILD BENEFIT CENTRE

Child Benefit Centre
Waterview Park
District 15, Washington
Tyne & Wear NE88 1ZB
Tel: 0300 200 3100
DX: 728800 Washington
Post to:

Child Benefit Office
PO Box 1
Newcastle-upon-Tyne NE88 1AA

COLLECTIVE INVESTMENT SCHEMES

The Collective Investment Schemes Centre (CISC) deals with all operational issues regarding Authorised Investment Funds, Investment Trust Companies, Unauthorised Unit Trusts, Pension Fund Pooling Schemes etc.

Collective Investment Schemes Centre
Local Compliance
Mid-size Business S0836
Newcastle NE98 1ZZ
Courier services should continue to deliver to:

HMRC Collective Investment Schemes Centre
3rd floor
Concept House
5 Young Street
Sheffield S1 4LB
Tel: 0300 053 6118 (Admin Team)
Fax: 0300 053 6169
Email: cisc.sheffield@hmrc.gsi.gov.uk

CONSTRUCTION INDUSTRY UNIT

Construction Industry Unit (London)
14th Floor, Euston Tower
286 Euston Road
London NW1 3UF
Post to: National Insurance Contributions and Employers Office, HM Revenue and Customs BX9 1BX
Helpline: 0300 200 3210
Fax: 0300 054 3730

CONSTRUCTION INDUSTRY SCHEME: BUSINESS BASED OUTSIDE UK

HM Revenue and Customs (HMRC) CIS team to register contractors or subcontractors based outside the UK:

Charities Savings and International 1
HM Revenue and Customs BX9 1AU
Tel: 03000 516644
Outside UK: +44 3000 516644

EMPLOYEE SHARES & SECURITIES UNIT

Employee Shares & Securities Unit
1st Floor, Fitzroy House
Castle Meadow Road
Nottingham NG2 1BD
Tel: 03000 550 826
email: shareschemes@hmrc.gsi.gov.uk
www.hmrc.gov.uk/shareschemes

ENFORCEMENT OFFICE

England and Wales
HMRC
Durrington Bridge House
Barrington Road
Worthing BN12 4SE
Fax: 0300 052 0360
DX: 90957 Worthing 3

Scotland
HMRC
Elgin House
20 Haymarket Yards
Edinburgh EH12 5WT
Tel: 0300 056 1693
Fax: 0300 056 1708

EXPATRIATE TEAMS
Division re-titled. Please see 'Personal Tax International' below.

FILM, PRODUCTION AND TV BROADCAST INDUSTRY

General PAYE and Self Assessment enquiries in the film, production and TV broadcast industry should be made in the first instance to the HMRC Contact Centre. Tel: 0300 200 3300.
All other enquiries, including actors, 7 Day Rule, expenses, employment status of grades, special letters or dispensations in the film and production industry should be made to:

Film and Production Unit
Floor 2
Weardale House
Washington
Tyne and Wear NE37 1LW
0300 123 2326
email: a.filmproductionunitmailbox
@hmrc.gsi.gov.uk
Employment status queries about workers engaged by television broadcasting companies should be addressed to:

TV Broadcasting Unit
4th Floor
Trinity Bridge House
2 Dearmans Place
Salford M3 5BH
Tel: 03000 510 191
email:
creative.industries@hmrc.gsi.gov.uk
Enquiries about workers engaged by foreign broadcasting companies should be addressed to:

Specialist Employer Compliance
Grayfield House
5 Bankhead Avenue
Edinburgh EH4 7DL
A specialist unit will deal with most claims for Film Tax Relief
(FTR); Corporation Tax affairs of most companies eligible for FTR; and queries about taxation of film production companies and FTR.
Cases dealt with by Large Business Service (mainly larger groups) will continue to be dealt with there.

Companies not entitled to FTR will be dealt with by their existing offices.

Manchester Film Tax Credit Unit
Local Compliance S0717
PO Box 3900
Glasgow G70 6AA
Tel: 03000 510 191
email: creative.industries@hmrc.gsi.co.uk

HIGH NET WORTH UNIT

The High Net Worth Unit (HNWU) deals with the tax affairs of HM Revenue and Customs' wealthiest individual customers. It aims to try and ensure they pay the right amount of tax and provide a single point of contact and a holistic approach to their tax affairs.
HNWU consists of around 440 staff in 32 customer teams based in Birmingham, Cardiff, East Kilbride, Edinburgh, London, Portsmouth, Shipley, Washington and Wrexham.

HM Revenue and Customs
High Net Worth Unit
SO 970
Newcastle upon Tyne NE98 1ZZ
Tel: 03000 528 549

LARGE BUSINESS SERVICE

Large Business Office (LBO) and Energy Group and Customs Large Business Group integrated to form a single HMRC Large Business Service (LBS). A new role of Customer Co-ordinator was introduced in 2010 as a result. The majority of large and complex customers who did not have a Customer Relationship Manager were assigned a Customer Co-ordinator.

LBS – SECTOR LEADERS

Large Business Director:
jo.wakeman@hmrc.gsi.gov.uk
Sectors and leaders:
North East
Agriculture, Food, Retail & Real Estate, Manufacturing:
max.hacon@hmrc.gsi.gov.uk
Scotland and Northern Ireland
Alcohol & Insurance:
graham.black@hmrc.gsi.gov.uk
London (1)

Banking: andrew.page@hmrc.gsi.gov.uk
North West
Business Services, Leisure & Media, Chemicals, Healthcare & Pharmaceuticals: chris.barker@hmrc.gsi.gov.uk
East Midlands
Construction & Transport:
louise.otterwell@hmrc.gsi.gov.uk
London (2)
Oil Gas, Automotive:
sara.obyrne@hmrc.gsi.gov.uk
South and Wales
Telecommunications, IT & Tobacco:
simon.forrester@hmrc.gsi.gov.uk
West Midlands
Utilities: frances.khan@hmrc.gsi.gov.uk
For general enquiries the Large Business Service Oil & Gas Sector can be contacted by post at:

HM Revenue and Customs
Large Business Service
Oil & Gas Sector
Bush House
South West Wing
Strand
London WC2B 4RD
Fax: 020 7438 6910

LIBRARY

The HMRC Library has now merged with other knowledge and communication departments. The library information service in its previous form is no longer available.

LONDON PAYE DIRECTIONS UNIT

(formerly Regulation 42(3)/49(5) Unit)
(Now under PAYE Direction Units)

MARKETING & COMMUNICATIONS

Press Office
2nd Floor Central
100 Parliament Street
London SW1A 2BQ
A full list of HMRC Press Office contacts can be found at
www.gov.uk/government/organisations/hm-revenue-customs/about/media-enquiries
(For matters previously dealt with by the Inland Revenue)

NATIONAL MINIMUM WAGE

National Minimum Wage enquiries
Freepost PHQ1
Newcastle-upon-Tyne NE98 1ZH
Tel (ACAS NMW Helpline): 0300 123
1100
www.gov.uk/your-right-to-minimum-
wage

NON-RESIDENTS RECOVERY UNIT

Centenary Court
1 St Blaise Way
Bradford BD1 4XX
Tel: 03000 538802
Fax: 0300 0584001

OIL TAXATION OFFICE
(See LBS Oil and Gas)

ONLINE SERVICES HELP DESK

Tel: 0300 200 3600
Fax: Faxes not accepted
minicom: 0300 200 3603
email: helpdesk@ir-efile.gov.uk
www.hmrc.gov.uk
www.gateway.gov.uk

PAYE DIRECTION UNITS

14th Floor, Euston Tower
286 Euston Road
London NW1 3UL

Wing D, Queensway House
Stewartfield Way
East Kilbride
Glasgow G79 1AA
Tel: 0300 200 3300

PENSION SCHEME SERVICES

HMRC Pension Schemes Services
Ferrers House
Castle Meadow Road
Nottingham NG2 1BD
Tel: 0300 123 1079
www.gov.uk/government/organisations/h
m-revenue-customs/contact/pension-sche
me-enquiries

PERSONAL TAX INTERNATIONAL
*This team now handles the tax affairs of
all inward expatriate employees — normally those working for multinational
organisations who are seconded or assigned to work in the UK. It also deals
with the employers of these individuals.
All PAYE correspondence should be sent
to:*

Manchester Expatriate Team
3rd Floor, West Wing
Trinity Bridge House
2 Dearmans Place
Salford M3 5BG
Tel: 0161 261 3398

Film Industry Group
*(See Film, Production and TV Broadcast
Industry)*

Foreign Entertainers' Unit
St John's House
Merton Road
Bootle L75 1BB
Tel: 0300 054 7395 (From abroad): +44
300 054 7395

IR35
(For an opinion on status)

IR35 Unit
Ground Floor North
Princes House
Cliftonville Road
Northampton NN1 5AE
IR35 Helpline: 0300 200 3885/0300
123 2326
email: IR35@hmrc.gov.uk
www.hmrc.gov.uk/IR35

Remittance Basis Charge Team
Unit 354, Room 200
St. John's House
Merton Road
Bootle L75 1BB

POST WAR CREDITS

Government Buildings
Ty Glas, Llanishen
Cardiff CF14 5ZN

RESIDENCY

HMRC Residency
St John's House Unit 358

Merton Road
Liverpool L75 1BB
Tel: 0300 123 1072
HMRC Residency has specialist staff
who will answer enquiries about non-
resident trusts.
**HM Revenue and Customs Residency –
further contacts:**
Individuals:
For income tax / capital gains tax enqui-
ries for customers who are living / going
to live abroad only.

Tel: 0300 200 3300
Tel (from abroad): +44 135 535 9022
*For National Insurance contributions-
related enquiries:*

Tel: 0300 200 3506
Crown Servants
(Crown servants: eg civil servants, diplo-
mats, members of the armed forces)
Dealt with by South Wales Area tax
offices.

Crown Servants
South Wales Area Residence Group
Ty Glas Road
Llanishen
Cardiff CF14 5FP
Tel: 0300 200 3300
Tel (from abroad): +44 135 535 9022
**Non-Resident Companies – claims under
double taxation treaties**

HMRC Residency
Ferrers House
PO Box 38
Nottingham NG2 1BB
Tel: 0300 200 3300

REVENUE POLICY
INTERNATIONAL REGISTRY

100 Parliament Street
London SW1A 2BQ

SHARES AND ASSETS VALUATION
(SAV)
SAV is responsible for the valuation of
unquoted shares and other assets for tax
purposes, for example copyrights, good-
will, bloodstock, livestock and under-
writing interests.

Shares and Assets Valuation
Ferrers House, PO Box 38
Castle Meadow Road
Nottingham NG2 1BB
Tel: 0300 123 1082
Fax: 0300 056 2705/0300 056 4567
DX: 701201 Nottingham 4

SMALL COMPANY
ENTERPRISE CENTRE
*(Enterprise Investment Schemes, Venture
Capital Trusts, Enterprise Manage-
ment Incentive, Corporate Venturing
schemes and Social Investment Tax
Relief.)*

Local Compliance
Small Company Enterprise Centre (Ad-
min team)
SO777 Newcastle NE98 1ZZ
Tel: 0300 123 1083
email:enterprise.centre@hmrc.gsi.gov.uk

SOLICITOR'S OFFICES

HMRC Solicitor's Office
3rd Floor
Bush House
Strand
London WC2B 4RD

SPECIALIST INVESTIGATIONS

Bristol
101 Victoria Street
Bristol BS1 6BG
Fax: 0300 052 2014

Liverpool
7th Floor
The Triad
Stanley Road
Bootle L75 2EE
Fax: 0151 933 9958

London
Angel Court
199 Borough High Street
London SE1 1HZ
(D)

Nottingham
Barkley House
PO Box 20
Castle Meadow Road

Nottingham NG2 1BA
DX: 726357 Nottingham 5

Solihull
2nd Floor, Royal House
Princes Gate
2–6 Homer Road
Solihull B91 3WG
DX: 726566 Solihull 26

Special Trade Investigation Unit
13th Floor, Euston Tower
286 Euston Road
London NW1 3TY
(D)

**Television Broadcasting and
Radio Companies**
*(For enquiries about workers engaged by
television companies. See also Film, Production and TV Broadcast Industry.)*

TV and Radio Unit
Chapel Wharf Area
Trinity Bridge House
2 Dearmans Place
Salford M3 5BS
Tel: 0300 200 3300

Tonnage Tax Unit
Local Compliance (Large & Complex)
Cherry Court
36 Ferensway
Hull HU2 8AQ

TAX CREDIT OFFICE
Tax credit renewal forms should go to
the address below, while new tax credit
claims should be sent to:
Tax Credit Office,
Liverpool L75 1AZ.

Comben House
Farriers Way
Netherton L75 1AX

TRUSTS AND ESTATES
Postal addresses for operational matters
are:

HMRC Trusts and Estates
Trusts
Meldrum House
15 Drumsheugh Gardens
Edinburgh EH3 7UQ

HMRC Trusts and Estates
Trusts
Ferrers House
Castle Meadow Road
Nottingham NG2 1BB
Tel: 0300 123 1072

HMRC Trusts and Estates
Trusts
Lysnoweth
Infirmary Hill
Truro TR1 2JD
Inheritance Tax
For written enquiries regarding inheri-
tance tax, which should include the full
name and date of death of the person
who has died:

HMRC Trusts and Estates
Inheritance Tax
Ferrers House
Castle Meadow Road
Nottingham NG2 1BB
Heritage Team
For further information regarding heri-
tage assets, please see
www.hmrc.gov.uk/inheritancetax/
conditionalexemption.pdf
The Trusts Helpline is 0300 123 1072
and is open from 9.00 am to 5.00 pm
Monday to Friday.

VAT RELIEF
For enquiries relating to VAT relief for
disabled and older people please write to
the following address:

VAT Disabled and Elderly Reliefs Corre-
spondence S0708
HM Revenue and Customs Charities,
Savings and International 2   BX9 1BU
Tel: 0300 123 1073 (selection option
'1')

VALUATION OFFICE AGENCY
Please note that the Valuation Office
Agency listings now appear on page 83.

**VOLUNTARY
ARRANGEMENTS SERVICE**

Durrington Bridge House
Barrington Road
Worthing BN12 4SE

Valuation Office Agency

The Valuation Office Agency (VOA) is an executive agency of HM Revenue and Customs which provides valuations and property advice to support taxation and benefits to the government and local authorities in England, Scotland and Wales. Most of its work involves compiling and maintaining rating and council tax lists for England and Wales. These lists form the basis for the business rates and council tax bills issued by local councils. District Valuer Services (DVS) is the property arm of the VOA.

To contact a local valuation office from England, Scotland and Northern Ireland: Tel: 0300 050 1501. From Wales: Tel: 0300 050 5505 (www.voa.go v.uk/corporate//contact/ceo/ceoOffice.html#address).

General VOA contact information:

Tel: 0300 050 1501 (England)
Tel: 0300 050 5505 (Wales)
(Available between 08.30am and 5.00pm.)

DVS general enquiries:

Tel: 0300 0500 400
email: dvscustomersupport@voa.gsi.gov.uk
Network Support Office – Housing Allowance, Fair Rent and Housing Benefit
VOA Rent Offices
Network Support Office
Wycliffe House
Green Lane
Durham DH1 3UW
Tel: 0300 050 2502
email: NSOhelpdesk@voa.gsi.gov.uk
Halifax Network Support Office
Third Floor
60 Crown Street
Halifax HX1 1HY
Plymouth Network Support Office
The Apex
Derriford Business Park
Brest Road
Plymouth PL6 5FL
Tel: 0300 050 1501
Rhyl Network Support Office
Llys Anwyl
Churton Road
Rhyl LL18 3NB

OFFICES

Head Office
Wingate House
93/107 Shaftesbury Avenue
London W1D 5BU
Tel: 0300 050 1501

Council Tax East
Ground Floor
Ferrers House
Castle Meadow Road
Nottingham NG2 1AB
Tel: 0300 050 1501
email: cteast@voa.gsi.gov.uk

Council Tax North
Manchester One
53 Portland Street
Manchester M1 3LD
Tel: 0300 050 1501
email: ctnorth@voa.gsi.gov.uk

Council Tax South
2nd Floor
1 Francis Grove
Wimbledon
London SW19 4DT
Tel: 0300 050 1501
email: ctsouth@voa.gsi.gov.uk

Council Tax Wales
Ty Glyder
339 High Street
Bangor LL57 1EP
Tel: 0300 050 5505
email: ctwales@voa.gsi.gov.uk

Council Tax West
2nd Floor
Overline House
Central Station
Blechynden Terrace
Southampton SO15 1GW
Tel: 0300 050 1501
email: ctwest@voa.gsi.gov.uk

Non-domestic Rates Central
2 Broadway
Broad Street
Birmingham B15 1BG
Tel: 0300 050 1501
email: ratingcentral@voa.gsi.gov.uk

Non-domestic Rates East
Roseberry Court
Central Avenue
St Andrews Business Park
Norwich NR7 0HS
Tel: 0300 050 1501
email: ratingeast@voa.gsi.gov.uk

Non-domestic Rates London
1st Floor, Lloyds Chambers
1 Portsoken Street
London E1 8BT
Tel: 0300 050 1501
email: ratinglondon@voa.gsi.gov.uk

Non-domestic Rates North East
6th Floor, Castle House
31 Lisbon Street
Leeds LS1 4DR
Tel: 0300 050 1501
email: ratingnortheast@voa.gsi.gov.uk

Non-domestic Rates North West
Redgrave Court
Merton Road
Bootle
Merseyside L20 7HS
Tel: 0300 050 1501
email: ratingnorthwest@voa.gsi.gov.uk

Non-domestic Rates South East
St Anne's House
2 St Anne's Road
Eastbourne BN21 3LG
Tel: 0300 050 1501
email: ratingsoutheast@voa.gsi.gov.uk

Non-domestic Rates South West
Temple Quay House
2 The Square
Temple Quay
Bristol BS1 6PN
Tel: 0300 050 1501
email: ratingsouthwest@voa.gsi.gov.uk

Non-domestic Rates Wales
Ty Rhodfa
Ty Glas Road
Llanishen
Cardiff CF14 5GR
Tel: 0300 050 5505
email: ratingwales@voa.gsi.gov.uk
Note: In Scotland council tax and business rates are dealt with by the Scottish Assessors. Full listings for council areas can be found at www.saa.gov.uk.

Scotland
District Valuer Scotland South-east
Elgin House
20 Haymarkets Yard

Edinburgh EH12 5WN
Tel: 0300 050 0400
email: scotlandse.vo@voa.gsi.gov.uk

Valuation Office Agency

Specialist Units for R&D Tax Credit Claims

HMRC has five specialist research and development (R&D) tax credit units. The units deal with all R&D tax credit claims from companies (apart from those dealt with by the Large Business Service (LBS)). The units cover claims from small and medium enterprises (SMEs) under *Finance Act 2000, Sch 20*, as well as claims by large companies under *Finance Act 2002, Sch 12* and claims to vaccine research relief under *Finance Act 2002, Sch 13*.

The aim of these specialist units is to improve the handling of claims by concentrating the work in a smaller number of locations staffed by specially trained officers, leading to greater consistency and providing more certainty for the companies making claims.

Background

R&D tax credits were introduced in 2000 for small and medium enterprises (SMEs), following extensive consultation with business, and extended to large companies in 2002.

They are a company tax relief which can either reduce a company's tax bill or, for some SMEs, provide a cash sum. The relief is not available to unincorporated businesses or partnerships.

The R&D tax credit works by allowing SMEs to deduct qualifying expenditure on R&D activities when calculating their profit for tax purposes. From 1 April 2015, the tax relief on allowable R&D costs is 230%. The previous rate was 225% from 1 April 2012.

SMEs can, in certain circumstances, surrender this tax relief to claim payable tax credits in cash from HMRC. Although the term 'tax credit' only strictly applies to the payable cash element available to SMEs, it also refers here to the enhanced deduction against profits.

Under the large company scheme, the rate of relief increased to 130% of qualifying expenditure (from 125%) from 1 April 2008.

Advance assurance for small companies

HMRC introduced Advance Assurance for companies that claim R&D tax relief in November 2015. If a company carries out R&D for itself or other companies, it could qualify for Advance Assurance.

This means that for the first three accounting periods of claiming for R&D tax relief, HMRC will allow the claim without further enquiries. Applying for Advance Assurance is voluntary and can be done at any time before the first claim for R&D tax relief.

The company can also still apply for R&D tax relief without Advance Assurance.

How to apply for advance assurance

To apply for Advance Assurance before your first claim for R&D tax relief, it is necessary to complete form CT R&D (AA). This can be done online or by filling in on-screen (you can save a partly completed form), then printing and posting it to HMRC.

Note that this form should not be used to make a claim for R&D tax relief or to make changes to an existing R&D tax relief claim.

Postal forms should be sent to:
Manchester R&D Unit
Local Compliance SO717
PO Box 3900
Glasgow
G70 6AA
Full details about the application process for advance assurance can be found at www.gov.uk/government/publications/research-and-development-tax-relief-application-for-advance-assurance-for-research-and-development-tax-relief-ct-rd-aa.

'Above the line' R&D expenditure credit (RDEC) scheme

The Large Company Scheme includes an 'above the line' credit which has been introduced for expenditure incurred on or after 1 April 2013. It will initially be optional, running alongside the enhanced deduction scheme which it will replace in April 2016. From 1 April 2015 relief is given at 11 per cent of qualifying R&D expenditure.

Relief is given as a taxable credit on the amount of qualifying R&D expenditure. The rules for identifying qualifying R&D activity and calculating R&D expenditure remain unchanged.

Further information

Further information on research and development relief is available on the HMRC website at www.gov.uk/guidance/corporation-tax-research-and-development-rd-relief.

Action required

In a departure from traditional practice where HMRC has normally allocated companies to tax offices on the basis of the address of the company's Registered Office, companies and agents should send corporation tax returns containing R&D tax credit claims to the specialist unit dealing with the postcode for the location of the main R&D activity of the company.

Companies and agents are also advised to state the location of their main R&D activity in claims to relief. This approach is designed to improve customer service.

There are four general exceptions to allocation by postcode. These are as follows.

- Companies dealt with by the LBS.
- Companies dealt with by the specialist pharmaceutical units in Manchester, Cambridge and Croydon should continue to send their returns to their current tax office. NB Pharmaceutical companies dealt with by the Reading office should now send their R&D claims to Southampton.
- companies dealt with by the SCECs (Small Company Enterprise Centres) in Maidstone and Cardiff should continue to send their returns to these offices.
- Companies dealt with by HMRC Charities in Bootle should continue to send their returns there.

(Companies in Wales, Scotland or Northern Ireland that are not in the four categories above should send their claims to the Cardiff unit.)

The intention is that in most cases the R&D specialist unit will deal with all aspects of a company's corporation tax return if it includes an R&D claim. This is similar to the approach HMRC already has in place for companies dealt with by the SCECs.

For a small number of very large companies or groups, where the R&D claim is only a relatively minor element of their tax affairs, the main tax office will stay the same, but the R&D claim will be handled with input from the appropriate specialist unit. These cases will be identified by the specialist units on a consistent basis, so companies which think they may be covered by this situation should follow the general advice to send their R&D claims to the appropriate specialist unit.

Agents or companies with specific questions about making R&D claims are encouraged to contact the appropriate specialist unit for advice:

Note – for the following offices, the main postal address is now:
PO Box 3900
Glasgow G70 6AA
Croydon R&D Unit
Local Compliance S1137

Leicester R&D Unit
Local Compliance S0563

Manchester R&D Unit
Local Compliance S0717

Portsmouth R&D Unit
Local Compliance S0793

Cardiff R&D Unit (Wales, Scotland and Northern Ireland)
Local Compliance S0970

CROYDON R&D UNIT

Local Compliance S1137
PO Box 3900
Glasgow G70 6AA
Tel: 0300 051 1811
email: Croydon.RandD@hmrc.gsi.gov.uk

LEICESTER R&D UNIT

Local Compliance S0563
PO Box 3900
Glasgow G70 6AA
Tel: 0300 051 5236
email: Leicester.RandD@hmrc.gsi.gov.uk

MANCHESTER R&D UNIT

Local Compliance SO717
PO Box 3900
Glasgow G70 6AA
Tel: 0300 051 0190
email:
randd.manchester@hmrc.gsi.gov.uk

PORTSMOUTH R&D UNIT

Local Compliance S0793
PO Box 3900
Glasgow G70 6AA
Tel: 0300 052 8835
email:
Portsmouth.RandD@hmrc.gsi.gov.uk

CARDIFF R&D UNIT (WALES, SCOTLAND AND NORTHERN IRELAND)

Local Compliance S0970
PO Box 3900
Glasgow G70 6AA
Tel: 0300 058 2420
email: Cardiff.randd@hmrc.gsi.gov.uk

Relevant R&D Units

From 1 July 2014, claims to R&D relief, R&D expenditure credit or Patent Box relief, made by companies who do not have a Customer Relationship Manager, will be dealt with by the office listed below, according to the claimant company's Registered Office.

AB	Cardiff		EX	Portsmouth
AL	Cardiff		FK	Cardiff
B	Cardiff		FY	Manchester
BA	Cardiff		G	Cardiff
BB	Manchester		GL	Cardiff
BD	Manchester		GU	Portsmouth
BH	Portsmouth		HA	Cardiff
BL	Manchester		HD	Manchester
BN	Portsmouth		HG	Manchester
BR	Croydon		HP	Portsmouth
BS	Cardiff		HR	Cardiff
BT	Manchester		HS	Cardiff
CA	Manchester		HU	Manchester
CB	Leicester		HX	Manchester
CF	Cardiff		IG	Cardiff
CH	Manchester		IP	Leicester
CM	Leicester		IV	Cardiff
CO	Leicester		KA	Cardiff
CR	Croydon		KT	Croydon
CT	Croydon		KW	Cardiff
CV	Leicester		KY	Cardiff
CW	Manchester		L	Manchester
DA	Croydon		LA	Manchester
DD	Cardiff		LD	Cardiff
DE	Leicester		LE	Leicester
DG	Cardiff		LL	Cardiff
DH	Manchester		LN	Leicester
DL	Manchester		LS	Manchester
DN	Leicester		LU	Leicester
DT	Portsmouth		M	Manchester
DY	Cardiff		ME	Croydon
E	Croydon		MK	Leicester
EC	Croydon		ML	Cardiff
EH	Cardiff		N	Croydon
EN	Cardiff		NE	Manchester

R&D Tax Claims

NG	Leicester	SS	Leicester
NN	Leicester	ST	Manchester
NP	Cardiff	SW	Croydon
NR	Leicester	SY	Cardiff
NW	Croydon	TA	Cardiff
OL	Manchester	TD	Cardiff
OX	Portsmouth	TF	Cardiff
PA	Cardiff	TN	Portsmouth
PE	Leicester	TQ	Portsmouth
PH	Cardiff	TR	Portsmouth
PL	Portsmouth	TS	Manchester
PO	Portsmouth	TW	Croydon
PR	Manchester	UB	Croydon
RG	Portsmouth	W	Croydon
RH	Portsmouth	WA	Manchester
RM	Leicester	WC	Croydon
S	Leicester	WD	Cardiff
SA	Cardiff	WF	Manchester
SE	Croydon	WN	Manchester
SG	Leicester	WR	Cardiff
SK	Manchester	WS	Leicester
SL	Portsmouth	WV	Cardiff
SM	Croydon	YO	Manchester
SN	Portsmouth	ZE	Cardiff
SO	Portsmouth		
SP	Portsmouth		
SR	Manchester		

Clearances and Approvals

Clearance Applications

Applications under any one or more of the undernoted provisions may be made in a single letter to the Clearances and Counteraction Team at the following address:

HM Revenue and Customs
CTIS Clearance SO483
Newcastle NE98 1ZZ
Email: reconstructions@hmrc.gsi.gov.uk

Market sensitive applications should be marked for the attention of 'The Team Leader'. Information that could affect the stock market price of a quoted company and information concerning the financial affairs of well-known individuals is regarded as sensitive.

Only one copy of the application is required and a single reply covering all the clearances will be given. The applicant should make it clear at the top of the letter which clearances are being requested.

If the applicant wishes to receive a reply by email he should write 'I confirm that our client understands and accepts the risks associated with email and that they are happy for you to send information concerning their business or personal details to us by email. I also confirm the email address(es) that I want you to use to contact us are . . . ' (adapted as appropriate). For security reasons HMRC is unable to send responses to market sensitive applications by email.

HMRC acknowledges only those applications that request an acknowledgement.

These arrangements cover:

Transactions in securities (CTA 2010 s 748, ITA 2007 s 701)

Application may be made for confirmation that HMRC is satisfied that one or more specified transactions are such that no counteraction notice ought to be served. In particular, HMRC will consider whether or not a main purpose of the taxpayer in being a party to the transaction(s), or any of them, is to obtain an income tax advantage or, as the case may be, a corporation tax advantage.

Demergers (CTA 2010 ss 1091, 1092)

In a company demerger, application may be made for an advance determination that a distribution is exempt or that a payment is not chargeable.

Purchase of own shares (CTA 2010 s 1044)

A company wishing to purchase some of its own shares can choose that the purchase is not treated as a distribution, but that instead the payments are brought into account for capital gains purposes only.

Reconstructions and amalgamations (TCGA 1992 ss 138, 139)

Where a scheme of company reconstruction or amalgamation involves the transfer of a UK resident company's business to another UK resident company for no consideration, capital assets are transferred at 'no gain, no loss' only where the scheme is undertaken for bona fide commercial reasons and not to avoid corporation tax, CGT or income tax.

Transfer of trade etc between companies in different EU states (TCGA 1992 ss 140A, 140B)

A special relief may be claimed where a qualifying company resident in one EU Member State transfers the whole or part of a trade or business carried on by it in the UK to a qualifying company resident in another EU Member State in exchange for securities in the latter company. On a claim, any assets included in the transfer are treated as transferred at no gain, no loss, provided amongst other things that the transfer is effected for bona fide commercial reasons.

Transfer of a non-UK trade etc between companies in EU states (TCGA 1992 ss 140C, 140D)

A relief similar to the above where the trade or business to be transferred is not in the UK.

Other

ITA 2007 s 247(1)(f) — Enterprise Investment Scheme (EIS) shares: confirmation that new shares will stand in the shoes of the old where EIS company is acquired by new company.

ITA 2007 s 257HB(1)(f) — Seed Enterprise Investment Scheme (SEIS) shares: confirmation that new shares will stand in the shoes of the old where SEIS company is acquired by new company.

CTA 2009 s 831 — confirmation of treatment of intangible assets on a reconstruction involving a transfer of the business.

CTA 2009 s 237 and, for income tax, *ITTOIA 2005 s 300* — confirmation of the taxpayer's view of the tax consequences of assigning a lease granted at undervalue.

CTA 2010 s 831 and, for income tax, *ITA 2007 s 770* — confirmation that a transaction in land is not regarded as being undertaken for the sole or main object of realising a gain on disposal.

CTA 2009 ss 426, 437, 677, 686 — confirmation that the reliefs for loan relationships and derivative contracts in *CTA 2009 Pt 5 Ch 13* and *Pt 7 Ch 9*

(European cross-border transfers of business) and *CTA 2009 Pt 5 Ch 14* and *Pt 7 Ch 10* (European cross-border mergers) will be applied.

TCGA 1992 ss 184G, 184H — confirmation that HMRC will not apply the targeted anti-avoidance rules to prevent income to capital converter schemes by companies.

TIOPA 2010 s 117(4) — confirmation that double tax reliefs will not be disapplied on cross-border transfers of loan relationships, derivative contracts or intangible fixed assets.

The arrangements detailed above do not cover the following:

Controlled foreign companies (CFCs)

Clearance applications under *TIOPA 2010 Pt 9A* and supporting documentation such as accounts should be sent electronically to mary.sharp@hmrc.gsi.gov.uk and copied to the UK group's Customer Relationship Manager or Customer Coordinator. No paper copies of an application are then needed. If it is not possible to send applications electronically, applications should be sent to:
CTIS, Foreign Profits Team Registry
(CFC clearances)
3rd Floor
100 Parliament Street
London SW1A 2BQ

Company migration

A UK resident company must give notice of its intention to cease to be resident in the UK and must present to HMRC for their approval the details of the arrangements it proposes to make for payment of tax liabilities (*TMA 1970 ss 109B–109F*).

Notifications should be sent to:
Nicola Harris
HM Revenue & Customs
CTIS Business International, Foreign
Profits Team
100 Parliament Street
London SW1A 2BQ
email: clearances.companymigration@hmrc.gsi.gov.uk

Advance Pricing Agreements (APAs)

Under *TIOPA 2010 ss 218–230*:

Application for (or expression of interest in) an Advance Pricing Agreement relating to transfer pricing issues (see Statement of Practice SP 2/10). Send application for agreement to:

HMRC Clearances

APA Team Leader (Dominic Vines)
HM Revenue & Customs
CTIS Business International
East Spur, Euston Tower
286 Euston Road
London NW1 3UH
Tel: 0300 058 5861
Fax: 0300 054 3795

Approvals

Qualifying life assurance policies

Applications for approval under *ICTA 1988 Sch 15* should be sent to:
HM Revenue & Customs
CTISA Corporation Tax and Business Income Tax
Financial Services Team
3rd Floor
100 Parliament Street
London SW1A 2BQ
Tel: 0300 058 5911

Enterprise Investment Scheme (EIS), Seed Enterprise Investment Scheme (SEIS), Venture Capital Trust (VCT) scheme and Social Investment Tax Relief (SITR)

The specialist staff at the Small Company Enterprise Centre can give advice on the workings of these schemes, as well as providing non-statutory advance assurance to companies and enterprises seeking investment under these schemes. Contact:
Local Compliance
Small Company Enterprise Centre Admin
Team
SO777
PO Box 3900
Glasgow G70 6AA
Tel: 0300 123 1083

Business investment relief

Foreign income or gains remitted to the UK by a person taxed on the remittance basis will be relieved from tax if invested by way of a qualifying investment within 45 days after being remitted (*ITA 2007 s 809VA*). Applications for advance clearance on whether a proposed investment can be treated as a qualifying investment should be sent to:

HM Revenue & Customs
Business Investment Relief Team S1278
BX9 1BN
Tel: 0300 052 7416

Creative industries

The specialist staff at the Creative Industries Unit can give advice on the workings of the scheme as it applies to Film Tax, Animation Tax, High-end Television Tax and Video Games Development Reliefs. Contact:

Creative Industries Unit (Film, Television/
Animation and Video Games Tax Reliefs)
Local Compliance S0717
PO Box 3900
Glasgow G70 6AA
Tel: 0300 051 0191

Inward investment

The Inward Investment Support aims to give clarity and certainty to non-UK resident businesses about the tax consequence of significant investment in the UK. By 'significant', HMRC usually mean investments intended to total £30 million or more, but they will assist on smaller investments which they agree may be of importance to the national or regional economy. To discuss the tax implications of the investment, write to:

Inward Investment Support
HM Revenue & Customs
CTISA Business International
100 Parliament Street
London SW1A 2BQ
email: inwardinvestmentsupport@hmrc.gsi.gov.uk

Stamp Duty Land Tax (SDLT)

If after reading the published guidance, a person is still unsure about how SDLT affects a transaction, he may contact the Stamp Taxes Helpline on 0300 200 3510 (or from outside the UK +44 1726 209 042). If they cannot answer the question they will advise the person to apply in writing to the Stamp Office for HMRC's written advice about how SDLT applies to the transaction. The address is:

Birmingham Stamp Office
9th Floor
City Centre House
30 Union Street
Birmingham B2 4AR

Other non-statutory clearances

If after fully considering the relevant guidance and/or contacting the relevant helpline, a person remains uncertain about HMRC's interpretation of recent tax legislation, he can ask HMRC for further guidance or advice. The letter should be headed 'Clearance Service'. HMRC will then set out their advice in writing. A checklist is provided at Annex A at www.gov.uk/government/publ ications/non-statutory-clearance-service-guidance-annexes to help decide what information should be provided.

If the taxpayer has a Customer Relationship Manager who is already in contact with an HMRC clearance team, the application should be sent directly to that person. Otherwise it should be sent to:

HMRC Non-Statutory Clearances Team
5th Floor
Alexander House
21 Victoria Avenue
Southend-on-Sea
Essex SS99 1AA
email: hmrc.southendteam@hmrc.gsi.gov.uk

HMRC will usually reply within 28 days. But where difficult or complicated issues are involved it may take longer. If this is the case, HMRC will acknowledge the request and inform the applicant when he can expect a full reply.

Where the clearance application relates to the inheritance tax business property relief consequences of a transaction, it should instead be sent (quoting the reference BP102/P1/08E) to:

HM Revenue & Customs
Trusts & Estates Technical Team
(Clearances)
Ferrers House
Castle Meadow Road
Nottingham NG2 1BB
email: mailpoint.e@hmrc.gsi.gov.uk

HMRC Complaints and Appeals

Making a complaint to HMRC

In the first instance, a complaint should be made to the office dealing with the taxpayer's affairs. If they are unable to help, the complainant will be referred to a customer service adviser. If the taxpayer is unhappy about speaking directly to the tax office concerned, the complaint can be referred to a customer service adviser from the outset.

Alternatively, a complaint can be made by telephone by calling the HMRC helpline that is relevant to the claim. The Helpline numbers are as follows.

Tax Credits Helpline	0345 300 3900
Self-Assessment Helpline	0300 200 3310
National Insurance Helpline	0300 200 3500
Child Benefit Helpline	0300 200 3100
VAT, Excise and Customs Helpline	0300 200 3700
Income Tax Helpline	0300 200 3300
Employer Helpline	0300 200 3200

Complaints can also be made in writing.

Complaints by post

To complain to HMRC about service in relation to Pay As You Earn (PAYE), the letter should be clearly marked as a complaint so that it can be directed to a complaints handler swiftly:
HM Revenue and Customs
PAYE & Self Assessment Complaints
BX9 1AB
For complaints about National Insurance or employers:
NIC and EO Complaints
HM Revenue and Customs
BX9 1AA
Couriers delivering post to a HMRC address with a PO box or BX postcode should use:
HM Revenue and Customs
Benton Park View
Newcastle Upon Tyne NE98 1ZZ

Make a complaint online

An employee or a pensioner who has had tax taken from their wage or pension, can use the trial online form to make a complaint. They will need to sign-in to or set up a Government Gateway account.

See www.tax.service.gov.uk/gg/sign-in?continue=%2Fforms%2Fform%2Fma ke-your-complaint-online%2Fnew&accountType=individual.

Self-assessment and PAYE suggested letter headings for agents

HMRC has identified some of the most common self-assessment and PAYE queries and has created a list of headings that can be used when sending letters about clients' affairs to HMRC. These headings enable HMRC to identify the broad content of a letter, decide whether specific technical input is required and allow them to ensure the correspondence reaches the right area. The primary headings summarise the broad subject of the letter, while the secondary headings can be used where the matter is more specific or requires more technical input. The list can be found at: www.gov.uk/agents-self-assessment-and-paye-letter-headings.

If the taxpayer is not happy with the way the complaint has been handled, they can ask for it to be reviewed by a different complaints handler. The response from the second complaints handler marks the end of HMRC's own complaints process. Any further complaints must be made to the Adjudicator.

Tax credits complaints

The complaint should be made to the person or office the claimant has been dealing with. Alternatively you can write to the Customer Service and Support Group (CSSG) who will provide a written response to the complaint:
Complaints
Tax Credit Office
Preston PR1 4AT

Serious misconduct by HMRC staff

If your complaint is about serious staff misconduct, such as assault or corruption, please follow the complaints process above. To contact an independent complaints coordinator, you can call 0300 057 7875 or write to:
HM Revenue & Customs
PO Box 64353
London EC3P 3AW

The complaint coordinators do not have the facility to help with any other HMRC matters. They will take details and pass them on to the relevant complaint handlers within HMRC to deal with. HMRC's handling of complaints of serious misconduct is overseen by the Independent Police Complaints Commission.

Adjudicator

If you have a complaint about the way in which HMRC has handled a case, you should first try to resolve the issue following the HMRC complaints procedure outlined above.

If the complaint cannot be settled in this way, you can approach the Adjudicator. The Adjudicator will look into complaints about HMRC including the Tax Credit Office, the Valuation Office Agency and The Insolvency Service.

Helen Megarry took up her new role as Independent Adjudicator with effect from 11 April 2016.

The Adjudicator acts as an impartial referee, by hearing both sides of a complaint, considering whether it is justified and making recommendations for putting matters right. The Adjudicator's recommendations are independent and her services are free.

The Adjudicator will look into complaints about:

- excessive delay;
- errors;
- poor or misleading advice;
- discourtesy; and
- the way in which HMRC has exercised its discretion.

She will not deal with appeals on matters of tax law, which are the province of the independent tribunals (see page 107).

Complaints can be made either in writing or by telephone, although an approach in writing is recommended. The address is:

The Adjudicator's Office
PO Box 10280
Nottingham NG2 9PF
Tel: 0300 057 1111 (9am–5pm, Monday to Friday)
Tel: 020 7667 1832 (typetalk facilities)
Fax: 0300 059 4513
DX: 147385 Piccadilly 7
www.adjudicatorsoffice.gov.uk
NB the office does not accept complaints or enquiries by email.

Complaints will not normally be examined if sent to the Adjudicator more than six months after the Area Director responsible has provided an unsatisfactory answer.

The Adjudicator also deals with complaints about the Valuation Office Agency and The Insolvency Service.

Parliamentary and Health Service Ombudsman

The Parliamentary Ombudsman, Dame Julie Mellor DBE, is an officer of the House of Commons and independent of the Government.

HMRC Complaints

If the complaint has been looked at by the Adjudicator, you can still ask your MP to refer it to the Ombudsman. The Adjudicator will not look at complaints which have been investigated by the Ombudsman, or which the Ombudsman is investigating.

You can also ask your MP to put any complaints about HMRC direct to the Ombudsman. You do not need to have referred your complaint first to the Adjudicator, though that would be the normal route.

Further information can be obtained from:
The Parliamentary and Health Service
Ombudsman
Millbank Tower
Millbank
London SW1P 4QP
Complaints Helpline: 0345 015 4033 (8.30am–5.30pm, Monday to Friday)
Call-back service: 07624 813 005
Textphone: 0300 061 4298
Fax: 0300 061 4000
email: phso.enquiries@ombudsman.org.uk
www.ombudsman.org.uk

To use the call back service, text 'call back' with your name and mobile number to 0762 481 3005. The text will be charged at the standard text rate. The Ombudsman will acknowledge your text at no cost and call back within one working day during office hours.

Appeals against an HMRC decision — direct tax

On occasions when you disagree with a decision made by HMRC, you may be able to challenge the decision by appealing. In most cases the appeal will be settled by reaching an agreement with HMRC. However, if this is not possible, one may request either of the following:

- a review by HMRC; or
- your appeal to be heard by an independent tribunal (see page 107).

Alongside the normal legal rights, a new option is now available in Alternative Dispute Resolution.

Alternative Dispute Resolution for SMEs and individuals

Alternative Dispute Resolution (ADR) is a new way of resolving disputes between HMRC and its customers. It has been introduced after a two year trial and extensive consultation with professional bodies and the voluntary sector.

This service aims to help resolve disputes or obtain agreement on which issues need to be taken for a legal ruling. To keep legal rights one should appeal or ask for statutory review as well asking for ADR. It is also possible to ask for ADR before HMRC have made a decision.

Richard Summersgill, HMRC Director of Local Compliance, announced the new service on 2 September 2013. He said: 'I am delighted to announce that

ADR for SMEs and individuals has entered mainstream HMRC business. Our customers have told us that they like the speed and flexibility of ADR. Evidence has shown that by using the simple ADR service many disputes can be significantly shortened and resolved without recourse to Tribunal.'

ADR is mainly aimed at helping business customers or those who have complicated personal tax affairs. ADR is not appropriate for disputes about:

- payments;
- fixed penalties on the grounds of reasonable excuse;
- tax credits;
- PAYE coding;
- claims for tax not to be collected under ESC A19; and
- cases being dealt with by HMRC's Criminal Investigators.

How it works

HMRC can arrange for someone who has not been involved in the case to work with the taxpayer or agent and the officer dealing with the case. The person leading the ADR is specially trained to act as a 'facilitator', a neutral third party mediator. They do not take over responsibility for a case.

The best time to apply for ADR is after all relevant facts have been established and an impasse has been reached.

The decision on settling a case stays with the agent and the officer handling the case. The person leading the ADR will work with them both to explore ways of resolving the dispute through meetings and telephone conversations. They will help focus on the areas that need to be resolved and, if needed, help re-establish dialogue. In some cases one might agree with HMRC to jointly pay for a professional independent mediator.

ADR cannot guarantee resolution of the dispute but by the end of the process, there should be clarity on the outstanding issues and what happens next.

How to ask for ADR

Large businesses should contact their Customer Relationship Manager or a dedicated caseworker. Small and medium sized businesses and personal taxpayers can use an online form to request ADR. Further information can be found at: www.gov.uk/tax-disputes-alternative-dispute-resolution-adr. Any other questions about ADR can be emailed to HMRC's Dispute Resolution Unit at: dispute.resolution@hmrc.gsi.gov.uk.

HMRC Complaints

Stamp Offices

Stamp duty land tax replaced stamp duty on land and buildings on 1 December 2003. It continues to be dealt with by HMRC Stamp Taxes, which is a business stream within HMRC Capital and Savings. NB Land and buildings transaction tax (LBTT) replaced UK stamp duty land tax (SDLT) in Scotland from 1 April 2015.

There is a Stamp Office enquiry line number: 0300 200 3510.

Land transaction returns, supplementary forms and guidance notes can be obtained from the orderline:

Tel: 0300 200 3511
email: saorderline.ir@gtnet.gov.uk
Post: IRCC, PO Box 37, St Austell PL35 5YN

STAMP DUTY LAND TAX TRANSACTION RETURN SUBMISSIONS (INCLUDING PAYMENTS)

HMRC SDLT
Comben House
Farriers Way
Netherton L30 4RN
DX: Rapid Data Capture Centre
DX: 725593 Bootle 9

BIRMINGHAM (GENERAL CORRESPONDENCE AND STAMP DUTY)

Birmingham Stamp Office
9th Floor, City Centre House
30 Union Street
Birmingham B2 4AR
Tel: 0300 200 3510
Fax: 030 0057 0316
DX: 15001 Birmingham 1
(Same day stamping open 8.30am-5.00pm Mon-Fri (bespoke service) not available for other enquiries). All other enquiries should be made to the Stamp Taxes Helpline. Tel: 0300 200 3510.

NEWCASTLE

15th Floor
Newcastle Stamp Office

Cale Cross House
156 Pilgrim Street
Newcastle upon Tyne NE1 6TF
DX: 61021 Newcastle upon Tyne 1

SCOTLAND (FOR SCOTTISH SOLICITORS ONLY)

Edinburgh Stamp Office
Elgin House
20 Haymarket Yards
Edinburgh EH12 5WN
Tel: 0300 200 3510
Fax: 030 0056 1703
DX: 543303 Edinburgh 33
(DX mail for Edinburgh should be marked with a blue cross on both sides of envelope)
(open Mon-Fri 9.30am-4.00pm)
Payments and notifications in respect of **stamp duty reserve tax** *should be sent to:*

SDRT (Operations)
9th Floor, City Centre House
30 Union Street
Birmingham B2 4AR
Tel: 0300 200 3510
Fax: 030 0057 0316
DX: 15001 Birmingham 1

Tribunals

Introduction

From April 2009, the previous Commissioners and Tribunals used by HM Revenue & Customs (HMRC) were replaced by the First-tier and Upper Tribunals, administered by the Ministry of Justice (MoJ). Her Majesty's Courts and Tribunals Service was created on 1 April 2011 to bring together Her Majesty's Courts Service and the Tribunals Service into one integrated agency providing support for the administration of justice and courts and tribunals. HM Courts and Tribunals Service is an agency of the Ministry of Justice responsible for the administration of criminal, civil and family courts and tribunals in England and Wales. The First-tier Tribunal comprises six chambers; the Tax Tribunal falls under the Tax Chamber, which also now covers MP expenses. The Upper Tribunal comprises four chambers. Tax matters are dealt with by the Upper Tribunal (Tax and Chancery) which is in the Tax and Chancery Chamber. The website is www.gov.uk/government/organisations/hm-courts-and-tribunals-service/about.

The First-tier Tribunal (Tax)

The Tax Chamber has a single set of procedural rules with flexibility for dealing with different kinds of cases. The rules (The Tribunal Procedure (First-tier Tribunal) (Tax Chamber) Rules 2009 (SI 2009/273) were subject to consultation and they can be accessed at: www.legislation.gov.uk/uksi/2009/273/contents/made

The First-tier Tribunal (Tax) hears appeals against decisions relating to tax made by HMRC. Appeals can be made by individuals or organisations, single tax payers or large multi-national companies. Appeals range from the relatively simple to the complex across both direct and indirect tax.

Appeals against HMRC decisions in relation to tax heard in the Tax Chamber include:

- Income Tax;
- Corporation Tax;
- Capital Gains Tax;
- Inheritance Tax;
- Stamp Duty Land Tax;
- PAYE coding notices;
- National Insurance contributions;
- Statutory Payments;
- VAT or duties such as custom duties, excise duties or landfill tax, aggregates or climate change levies; and
- the amounts of tax or duty to be paid, against penalties imposed upon them and against certain other decisions.

You can also make applications to the tribunal if, for example, HMRC refuses to accept a late direct tax appeal or an indirect tax hardship application.

If HMRC is carrying out an enquiry into your business's direct tax affairs, you can ask the tribunal to tell HMRC to close that enquiry, if you don't think it's reasonable for them to continue.

NB: Appeals against decisions in relation to tax credits are heard by the First-tier Tribunal (Social Security and Child Support) (www.justice.gov.uk/tribunals/sscs).

The First-tier Tribunal (Charity)

The *Charities Act 2006* established the Charity Tribunal, which now falls under the General Regulatory Chamber.

The First–tier Tribunal (Charity) can:

- hear appeals against the decisions of the Charity Commission (the Commission);
- hear applications for review of decisions of the Charity Commission; and
- consider references from the Attorney General or the Charity Commission on points of law.

General Regulatory Chamber
HM Courts and Tribunals Service
PO Box 9300
Leicester LE1 8DJ
Tel: 030 0123 4504
Fax: 0116 249 4253
email: grc@hmcts.gsi.gov.uk

A useful guide to the Charity Tribunal has been produced by the National Council for Voluntary Organisations and can be downloaded from blogs.ncvo.org.uk/wp-content/uploads/elizabeth-chamberlain/NCVO-The-Charity-Tribunal.pdf

The Upper Tribunal

The Upper Tribunal (Tax and Chancery) is a Superior Court of Record with UK-wide jurisdiction. It consists of specialist judges whose main work is to decide applications for permission to appeal and appeals on points of law from decisions of the First-tier Tribunal (Tax) as well as matters relating to certain decisions of the Financial Conduct Authority and the Pensions Regulator. The chamber also has the power of judicial review in certain circumstances.

The judiciary of the Upper Tribunal (Tax and Chancery) are High Court judges as well as specialist tax, charity and finance judiciary.

Mrs Justice Rose is the president of the chamber.

The office addresses are as follows.

First-tier Tribunal (Tax Chamber)
HM Courts & Tribunals Service
PO Box 16972
Birmingham B16 6TZ
Tel: 0300 123 1024 (8.30 am–5.00 pm)
email: taxappeals@hmcts.gsi.gov.uk
www.justice.gov.uk/tribunals/tax
The Upper Tribunal (Tax and Chancery
Chamber)
5th Floor, 7 Rolls Building
Fetter Lane
London EC4A 1NL
DX: 160042 Strand 4
Tel: 020 7612 9730
Fax: 0870 324 0172
email: uttc@hmcts.gsi.gov.uk

There are four venues for appeals hearings. These are listed below.
Tribunals Service
Tax
45 Bedford Square
London WC1B 3DN
Tel: 020 7612 9700
Fax: 0207 436 4150 / 4151
email: taxappealslon@tribunals.gsi.gov.uk
Tribunals Service
Tax
Alexandra House
14-22 The Parsonage
Manchester M3 2JA
Telephone: 0161 833 6100
Fax: 0161 832 0249/0870 739 4433
email: taxappealsman@tribunals.gsi.gov.uk
Tribunals Service
Tax
George House
126 George Street
Edinburgh EH2 4HH
Tel: 0131 271 4330
Fax: 0131 271 4399
email: taxappealsscot@tribunals.gsi.gov.uk
First-tier Tribunal (Tax Chamber) / Upper
Tribunal (Finance & Tax Chamber)
3rd Floor
Temple Court
4th Floor, 54 Hagley Road
PO Box 16972
Birmingham B16 6TZ
Tel: 0300 123 1024
email: taxappeals@tribunals.gsi.gov.uk

The Channel Islands, Ireland and the Isle of Man

The expression 'United Kingdom' means England, Scotland, Wales and Northern Ireland; it does not include the Isle of Man or the Channel Islands.

The addresses of the main tax authorities in these states are as follows.

CHANNEL ISLANDS

The Director
Income Tax Office
PO Box 37
2 Cornet Street
St Peter Port
Guernsey GY1 3AZ
Tel: 01481 724 711
Fax: 01481 713 911
www.gov.gg/tax
email: enquiries@tax.gov.gg

Jersey Comptroller of Income Tax
PO Box 56
Cyril Le Marquand House
The Parade
St Helier
Jersey JE4 8PF
Tel: 01534 440 300
Fax: 01534 724 315
www.gov.je/taxmoney
email: jerseytax@gov.je

IRELAND (REPUBLIC OF IRELAND)

The Revenue Commissioners
Dublin Castle
Dublin 2
Tel: 00 353 16 475000
www.revenue.ie

ISLE OF MAN

Isle of Man Assessor of Income Tax
Bucks Road
Government Offices
Douglas IM1 3TX
Tel: 01624 685 400
Fax: 01624 685 351
www.gov.im/treasury/incometax
email: incometax@gov.im

VAT OFFICE

Douglas
PO Box 6
Custom House
North Quay
Douglas IM99 1AG
Tel: 01624 648 130
Fax: 01624 661 725
www.gov.im/customs
email: customsgov.im

Channel Islands, Etc.

National Insurance Contributions Office Structure

The National Insurance Contributions Office (NICO) is responsible for safeguarding and maintaining accurate National Insurance accounts.

As part of HMRC's wider Service Delivery Team, it works closely with HMRC Local Services, Large Business Office, Share Pensions Savings Schemes Office and all the National Business Streams. It also has strong links with DWP.

NI Services to Contributor Group
The Contributor Group contains the following business units:

- Self-employment services, dealing with class 2 and class 3 contributions;
- Deferment services, responsible for preventing overpayment where there is more than one source of income;
- Processing centre, which deals with straightforward applications to register as self-employed and awards certificates of small earnings exception;
- International services, administers legislation governing people living or working abroad;
- Record Retrieval Section (formerly Special section A), which provides contribution and employment details to certain other government departments;
- NI Registrations, creates NI records for those not previously registered;
- Account Investigation Section, which monitors the accuracy of NI accounts;
- Refunds;
- Individuals Caseworker, dealing with cases with a shortfall in contributions, and exempt or reduced rate cases; and
- Home Responsibilities Protection where the number of qualifying years for a basic pension may be reduced. (For further information see www.gov.uk/government/publications/national-insurance-application-form-for-home-responsibilities-protection-cf411.)

Contact details (all areas):
National Insurance Contributions and Employer Office
Individuals Caseworker
Benton Park View
Newcastle-upon-Tyne NE98 1ZZ

You should quote your National Insurance number in all correspondence.

National Insurance International Services Helpline:
Tel: 0300 200 3500
Tel (from abroad): +44 191 203 7010

National Insurance Registrations Helpline:
Tel: 0300 200 3500

National Insurance Self-Employed Helpline:
Tel: 0300 200 3500

Newly Self-Employed Helpline:
Tel: 0300 200 3500

NI Services to Employer Group

The National Insurance Services to Employer Group covers all work relating to Class 1 National Insurance contributions and contains the following business units:

- Paper End of Year Processing (PEOYP);
- Electronic End of Year Processing (EEOYP);
- Caseworker, investigating category and liability for class 1 contributions; and
- NI Integrity, which investigates anomalies concerning NI numbers and accounts, and potential fraud referrals.

The NI Services to Employer Group can be contacted by telephone on 0300 200 3500.

NI Services to Pensions Industry

The NI Services to Pensions Industry (NISPI) is a Directorate within NICO, based in Newcastle. NISPI deals with occupational pension schemes and Appropriate Personal Pension (APP) schemes that are contracted-out of the state additional pension (AP). It is divided into three main business areas:

- Contracted-Out Early Leavers Section (COEL), Payments and Pension Account Maintenance (PAM);
- Retirement Pension/Widows Benefit (RP/ WB), Contracted-out Money Purchase (COMP) and Personal Pensions (PP);
- Scheme Cessations/Elections when COMP and COMB schemes cease to contract-out (contracted-out schemes are dealt with at the HMRC Audit and Pension Scheme Services (APSS) in Nottingham); and
- Customer Account Management (CAM).

There is also a Pensions Technical and Support Team. Pensions Technical deals with policy, appeals and complex cases. The Support Team provides regular information and updates about changes.

HMRC launched the Scheme Reconciliation Service (SRS) in April 2014 to help pension scheme administrators and trustees reconcile their records for all non-active members against HMRC records in advance of the ending of contracting-out in April 2016. Schemes must have registered to use the SRS before 5 April 2016. HMRC will continue to offer support to deal with any queries up until December 2018.

The 5 April 2016 cut-off date has passed. However, HMRC will consider Expressions of Interest submitted by PSAs after 5 April. Each application will be treated on its merits basis and these requests must be submitted in writing, via email, to crm.schemereconciliationservice@hmrc.gsi.gov.uk detailing the circumstances leading to the late submission.

There are a number of email addresses for pensions enquiries:

- for enquiries about National Insurance Services to Pensions Industry (NISPI) magnetic media services: nispi.magmedia@hmrc.gsi.gov.uk;
- for scheme cessation Shared Workspace enquiries: sharedworkspace.schemecessation@hmrc.gsi.gov.uk;
- for general enquiries about the Scheme Reconciliation Service: mailbox.newstatepensionenquiries@hmrc.gsi.gov.uk; and

- for general enquiries about data in your Scheme Reconciliation e-Room: schemereconciliationsw.inbox@hmrc.gsi.gov.uk.

NISPI guidance can be accessed at www.gov.uk/government/collections/nispi-guidance and www.gov.uk/government/collections/national-insurance-services-to-pensions-industry-countdown-bulletins.

Major units are listed on pages 117–119.

NIC Offices

Special NIC Offices

Most of the specialised groups of the National Insurance Contributions Offices operate from HMRC National Insurance Contributions Office, Benton Park View, Benton Park Road, Longbenton, Newcastle upon Tyne NE98 1ZZ. The simplified postal address is now: National Insurance Contributions and Employer Office, HM Revenue and Customs BX9 1AN, and for complaints: NIC and EO Complaints, HM Revenue and Customs BX9 1AA. Tel: 0300 200 3500.

Contact details for particular sections are given below with full addresses where not located in Central Office. In addition, other useful helplines are listed on page 121.

Accounts Office, Newcastle

The payment and collection of National Insurance contributions are now dealt with by the Revenue's Receivables Management business stream via Accounts Office, Newcastle at the above address and phone number.

This Accounts Office comprises:

- Newcastle Banking Unit (was Central Banking Services);
- Debt Management Services;
- Insolvency Claims Handling; and
- Civil Recoveries Section.

The details of these departments are included in the list below.

Civil Recoveries Section (Newcastle)

This section is the Solicitor's office for the NICO. The CRS controls the collection of debts referred to it, or arranges for court proceedings.

For further details contact:
HMRC
Accounts Office Newcastle
Banking of Debt Management
Civil Recoveries Section
Benton Park View
Newcastle upon Tyne NE98 1ZZ

Class 1 Caseworker Group
Customer Services Manager
Class 1 Caseworker
Room BP 1202
Tel: 0300 056 0629

NIC Offices

Contracted-out Employment Group (COEG)

Chillingham House
Benton Park View
Newcastle upon Tyne NE98 1ZZ

Debt Management Services (DMS)

DMS controls all Quarterly Billing debts of £150 or more. The Debt Management System contacts contributors with unpaid debts over 28 days old. If no contact can be made, or debts remain outstanding, cases are referred to the Civil Recoveries Section in Newcastle (see above).

Revenue NICO
Debt Management Services
Long Benton
Newcastle upon Tyne NE98 1ZZ
Tel: Contact local office
DX: 713266 Newcastle 17

Large Business Service

(See Large Business Service on page 79.)

Letter Forwarding Service (DWP)

The Department for Work and Pensions (DWP) provide a letter forwarding service for pension scheme administrators and providers. Schemes can use this service to trace individuals who have entitlement to contracted-out rights.

DWP charges for this service. Further details are available at: www.gov.uk/government/uploads/system/uploads/attachment_data/file/233042/bulk-letter-forwarding-leaflet.pdf.

Marine NICs (Cardiff)

HM Revenue and Customs
15th Floor East Wing
Ty Glas
Llanishen
Cardiff CF14 5FP
Tel: 0300 058 2419
Fax: 02920 756 016

Newcastle Banking Unit

All payments made by cheque, postal order or cash to NICO head office are referred to Newcastle Banking Unit (was Central Banking Services) for allocation to the appropriate section.
Central Banking Services Manager
Room BP 5002
NI Contributions Office
Longbenton NE98 1ZZ

Record Retrieval Section (formerly Special Section A)

From 1 February 2012 the renamed team, which deals with compensation claims for solicitors/individual customers, can be contacted at:
HM Revenue and Customs
National Insurance Contributions & Employer Office
Record Retrieval Service
Room BP8003
Tynemouth House
Benton Park View
Longbenton NE98 1ZZ

HMRC Residency
HM Revenue and Customs
NICO International Caseworker
Room BP1301
Benton Park View
Newcastle-upon-Tyne NE98 1ZZ
Non-residents helpline: 0300 200 3500
Tel (outside UK): +44 191 203 7010

HMRC Statutory Payments Team
Howard House
Castle Meadow Road
Nottingham NG2 1AB
Tel: 0300 200 3200

NIC Offices

Other Useful National Insurance Office Telephone Numbers

Age Exemption Helpline	Tel: 0300 200 3500
Contracted out Pensions Helpline	Tel: 0300 200 3500
	Textphone: 0300 200 3519
Deficiency Notice Helpline	Tel: 0300 200 3500
	Textphone: 0300 200 3519
Employers' Helpline (existing employers)	Tel: 0300 200 3200
	Textphone: 0300 200 3212
General NI enquiries	Tel: 0300 200 3500
HMRC call centre,	
International Caseworkers Helpline	Tel: 0300 200 3500
	From outside the UK dial the international code and then 44 191 203 7010
National Insurance: Registrations Helpline	Tel: 0300 200 3500
	Textphone: 0300 200 3519
National Insurance: Self-employed Helpline	Tel: 0300 200 3500
New entrants to the UK	Tel: 0345 6000 643
New employers Helpline	Tel: 0300 200 3211
Non-UK residents	Tel: 0300 200 3500
	Tel from abroad: +44 191 203 7010
	To speak to someone in Welsh: 0300 200 1900
Pension forecast Helpline	Tel: 0345 3000 168
Self-employed Helpline:	Tel: 0300 200 3500
	Textphone: 0300 200 3519
Stationery order line (national)	Tel: 0300 123 1074
Tax Credit Helpline (national)	Tel: 0345 300 3900
Welsh Language Helpline	Tel: 0300 200 1900

NIC Offices

HMRC – Enforcement

Two independent agencies cover the area of enforcement.

1. Specialist Fraud Division of the Crown Prosecution Service

The Specialist Fraud Division (SFD), which incorporates the Revenue and Customs Division (RCD) and the Fraud Prosecution Division (FPD), prosecutes all criminal tax, excise and strategic export cases which are subject to criminal investigations by HMRC. SFD also covers all criminal cases relating to benefits and child maintenance legislation which are investigated by the Department of Work and Pensions (DWP), NHS fraud investigated by NHS Protect, and more. It employs around 255 prosecutors, paralegals and administrators based across offices in Manchester, Leeds, Liverpool, Birmingham, Cardiff and London. For queries about the work of the SFD, contact the Division's enquiry team at SFD.Enquiries@cps.gsi.gov.uk.

The Crown Prosecution Service (CPS) has two other casework divisions, each with its own specialism. They are the Organised Crime Division and the Special Crime and Counter Terrorism Division.

London office:
Rose Court
2 Southwark Bridge
London SE1 9HS
Tel: 020 3357 0000
email: enquiries@cps.gsi.gov.uk
www.cps.gov.uk/your_cps/our_organisation

Manchester office:
PO Box 237
8th Floor
Sunlight House
Quay Street
Manchester M60 3PS
DX No: 744372 Manchester 53
Tel: 0161 827 4700

York office:
Foss House
Kings Pool
1–2 Peasholme Green
York YO1 7PX
Tel: 01904 545400

2. National Crime Agency

The National Crime Agency (NCA) became operational in October 2013.

The NCA is an operational crime fighting agency intended to tackle organised crime, strengthen borders, fight fraud and cyber-crime and protect children and young people. It will build on the work of SOCA, the Child Exploitation and Online Protection Centre, and incorporates some functions of the National Policing Improvement Agency.

The NCA has four 'Commands':

- Organised Crime Command;
- Economic Crime Command;
- CEOP Command (Child Exploitation and Online Protection); and
- Border Policing Command (now part of the Intelligence and Operations Directorate along with the National Intelligence Hub).

The NCA also has the National Cyber Crime Unit.

Economic Crime Command

The Economic Crime Command leads the national response to economic crime threats including fraud; bribery and corruption; intellectual property crime; identity crime; criminal finances and money laundering. It also co-ordinates investigation and seizure of criminal assets and works closely with partners across law enforcement and the public and private sectors.

The Joint Money Laundering Intelligence Taskforce (JMLIT) was set up in 2015 as a one-year pilot, in partnership with the financial sector to combat high end money laundering. However, it is to become a permanent part of the response to money laundering. The taskforce will analyse information and expertise in the public and private sectors to better understand the true scale of money laundering and the methods used by criminals to exploit the UK's financial system and will then agree actions that stop it. JMLIT involves over 20 major UK and international banks under the leadership of the 'Financial Sector Forum' and is delivering a wide range of benefits, including a more informed prioritisation of risk by the banks; targeted intervention by law enforcement and greater opportunities to learn from partners' approaches.

Border Policing Command

The Border Policing Command (BPC) brings the NCA's overseas border capability into a single operational response. Their main aim is to disrupt and prevent serious and organised crime across the NCA remit and support UK partners before it impacts the UK either upstream or at the UK border. The BPC leads the UK's effort to secure our borders and prevent criminals and terrorists evading border controls. It also coordinates all UK enforcement assets overseas to ensure they have the greatest possible impact.

The command consists of four key desks:

- The **NCA overseas network** supports overseas work and the Military and Maritime Intervention Cell. The overseas network builds on the existing excellent reputation, broadening its remit, its support for partners and its ability to work more closely with other UK assets overseas, who continue to deliver a large part of the volume of the NCA's seizures and arrests.

- The **Border Investigations Team** lead investigations at the border, including all Border Force detections of drugs, firearms, cash and other non-fiscal crime. They continue to deliver successful prosecutions and can be tasked to support NCA and partner operations as well.
- The multi-agency **Joint Border Intelligence Units** along with Ports Special Branch, Border Force and Her Majesty's Revenue & Customs, provides the UK law enforcement intelligence response to events at the border, debriefing and joining together intelligence for the benefit of all our partners.
- A small team at the centre of the BPC drives multi-agency work to improve border security. The team tasks the Joint Border Security Risk Assessment and develops and drives the Joint Border Control Strategy.

Full information about the NCA can be found at: www.nationalcrimeagency .gov.uk. The postal address for NCA headquarters is:
Units 1-6 Citadel Place
Tinworth Street
London SE11 5EF
Tel: 0370 496 7622

The telephone number for NCA is available at all times on all days. This covers general enquiries or to verify a person as an NCA officer. General enquiries can also be emailed to communication@nca.x.gsi.gov.uk.

Suspicious Activity Reports (SARs)

The UK Financial Intelligence Unit (UKFIU), now part of the NCA, is responsible for receiving, analysing and disseminating financial intelligence submitted through the Suspicious Activity Reports (SARs) system. The Unit receives over 200,000 SARs a year. According to HMRC, around a fifth of SARs received identify a new subject of interest and a quarter lead to new enquiries in relation to direct taxation matters.

The UKFIU also produces guidance documents produced by the UKFIU include 'Completing a SAR', 'Introduction to SARs', 'Reporting via SAR Online' and 'SAR Training Case Studies'.

The *Proceeds of Crime Act 2002 (POCA 2002)* expanded and consolidated the UK's criminal money laundering offences. Most offences under the Act apply to all individuals and businesses in the UK, though some apply only to those in the 'regulated sector'.

The Money Laundering Regulations 2007 (SI 2007 No 2157) cover a wide range of businesses and individuals providing goods and services where cash may be used in transactions. *POCA 2002 Sch 9* lists the types of activity which would bring a business within the regulated sector. These include credit and financial institutions, auditors, insolvency practitioners, external accountants, tax advisers etc. As soon as you 'know' or 'suspect' that a person is engaged in money laundering or dealing in criminal property, you must submit a SAR.

NCA's preferred method for people to report suspicions is the NCA Suspicious Activity Report Form using its secure online system (which requires registration). The form can also be submitted by fax or by post. Hard copy versions of the NCA-preferred forms (including Limited Intelligence Value Reports) can be found on the NCA website or obtained by phoning NCA's SAR helpdesk. These can be posted to the address below. Hard copy consents should be faxed to 020 7238 8286.

NCA SAR Online System: The main website links to this. It is also possible to link to the form from the government website (www.gov.uk/money-launderin g-regulations-report-suspicious-activities).

SAR helpdesk: Tel: 020 7238 8282

SAR Confidentiality Breach Line: There is a dedicated line to raise any concerns about the inappropriate use of SARs (by end users) or breaches of SAR confidentiality. Tel: 0800 234 6657 (9:00 – 17:00 Monday – Friday).

SARs can be submitted by post to the following address (NB no acknow-ledgement will be sent out):
UKFIU
PO Box 8000
London SE11 5EN
Tel (24 Hrs): 0370 496 7622
For general UKFIU matters email: ukfiusars@nca.x.gsi.gov.uk

Full information about submitting SARs can be found at: www.nationalcrim eagency.gov.uk/contact-us/reporting-suspicious-activity-sar.

Money Laundering Regulations and Supervised Businesses Register

Wherever possible HMRC recommends that any questions about money laundering regulations are submitted by email. HMRC can reply to your question more quickly this way. However, it notes that it cannot guarantee the security of emails sent over the internet. Email enquiries about money laundering regulations should be sent to MLRCIT@hmrc.gsi.gov.uk or phone 0300 200 3700.

Further information about businesses which need to register for HMRC supervision is available at: www.gov.uk/guidance/money-laundering-regulatio ns-introduction.

The Supervised Business Register at https://customs.hmrc.gov.uk/msbregister/ checkTerms.do can be used to verify that a Money Service Business or Estate Agency Business is registered with HM Revenue and Customs (HMRC) for su pervision under the Money Laundering Regulations. However, it should be noted that confirmation that a business is registered with HMRC is not an en dorsement.

Ideally post should only be used to send a form or a more complicated query that needs an answer. The address is:

HMRC Anti Money Laundering Supervision
Alexander House
21 Victoria House
Southend-on-Sea SS99 1AG

Voluntary disclosure of tax fraud

A taxpayer who wishes to own up to fraud voluntarily, will need to complete form CDF1 and send it to HMRC. It would be sensible to obtain independent advice before doing so. The form requests HMRC to consider offering a Contractual Disclosure Facility (CDF) arrangement for disclosing tax fraud.

Further information and form CDF1 can be found at www.gov.uk/government/publications/voluntary-disclosure-contractual-disclosure-facility-cdf1. The CDF Helpline is open from 10am to 3pm, Monday to Friday; tel: 0300 057 9336.

The form must be fully completed before it can be printed. It is important to gather all the information together before beginning the form as a partly completed form cannot be saved.

The completed form should be sent to:
HM Revenue and Customs
Fraud Investigation Service
COP9 Centre
S0828
Newcastle NE98 1ZZ

HMRC Enforcement

Value Added Tax

The department administers the collection of VAT, Excise and other duties formerly dealt with by HM Customs & Excise (HMCE).

VAT Registration and Deregistration

VAT registration should normally be done online (the form can be accessed at: www.gov.uk/vat-registration/how-to-register).

However, forms can be printed and submitted by post to the registration section at the address below:
HM Revenue & Customs
VAT Registration Service
Crown House
Birch Street
Wolverhampton WV1 4JX

Applications to register a VAT group (VAT1 with VAT50, VAT51) or applications to register where wishing to keep the previous owner's VAT number (VAT1 with VAT68), or where the applicant has temporarily exceeded the registration threshold and wants to ask for an exception so that they don't have to register for VAT should be sent to:
HM Revenue & Customs
VAT Registration Service
Imperial House
77 Victoria Street
Grimsby DN31 1DB
Tel: 0300 200 3700

Changing your VAT registration details or deregistering from VAT — postal address

All letters and forms relating to notification of changes in details, or requests for cancellation of registration (VAT7) should be sent to the central post room at Grimsby. If a reply or further information is needed then a response will be sent from the team at Wolverhampton.

To speak to someone in respect of changes in details, or a request for cancellation of registration, phone 0300 200 3700.

Partnerships

To register a partnership, you also have to complete form VAT2 to tell HMRC who the partners are. *This is not currently available to complete online* but can be downloaded from HMRC's website.

If you applied for VAT registration online, you download and post a VAT2 as above but need to write the acknowledgement number from the VAT1 on the VAT2.

A group of companies

The application forms to register a group of companies can be downloaded, but the *registration cannot currently be completed online*. The forms must be printed out and sent to HMRC VAT Registration Service at Grimsby.

How to register for VAT if you do business internationally

- If you acquire goods from other EU countries and the value of those goods is over the current registration threshold you must register for UK VAT. You can download the application form to register for VAT for acquisitions, but the registration cannot currently be completed online. The form must be printed out for completion, and then sent to the Wolverhampton address.
- This also applies to VAT registration applications for EU businesses 'distance selling' to UK customers, where the value of their distance sales is more than £70,000 in a year.
- Businesses that do not have a UK place of business, but sell to UK customers, must register as a Non-Established Taxable Person (NETP). You can download the application form VAT1 to register for VAT as a Non Established Taxable Person (NETP), but your registration cannot currently be completed online. You must print the form, complete it, and then send it to the Aberdeen office.
- This also applies to registering for VAT if a firm sells, supplies or otherwise disposes of an asset on which someone has claimed – or intends to claim – an 8th or 13th Directive refund.

VAT Mini One Stop Shop (VAT MOSS)

From 1 January 2015 the VAT rules for place of supply changed in the EU for sales of digital services from businesses to consumers. (The change doesn't affect business to business sales.) If a business sells digital services to consumers in EU member states, VAT is charged at the rate due in the consumer's country.

To pay the VAT due on these sales firms can either:

- register for VAT in each EU country where they supply digital services to consumers; or
- use the VAT MOSS scheme in one EU country.

There are two types of scheme: Union VAT MOSS – for businesses based in the EU (including the UK) and Non-Union VAT MOSS – for businesses based outside of the EU.

For full details of the procedures, see: www.gov.uk/guidance/register-and-use-the-vat-mini-one-stop-shop.

(See page 133 onwards for details of VAT office addresses, etc.)

Grimsby Registration Unit
HM Revenue & Customs
Imperial House
77 Victoria Street
Grimsby DN31 1DB
Tel: 0300 200 3700

Wolverhampton Registration &
Deregistration Unit
HM Revenue & Customs
Crown House
Birch Street
Wolverhampton WV1 4JX

Non Established Taxable Persons Unit
HM Revenue & Customs
Ruby House
8 Ruby Place
Aberdeen AB10 1ZP
Tel: 0300 0521 260
(general enquiries)
Tel: 0300 0521 261
(registration)
Fax: 0300 052 1408

VAT Offices
(including national operations)

National Advice Service Helpline: 0300 200 3700

VAT offices deal with administration of VAT in their area, but not the issue of return forms or the receipt of VAT which is dealt with by the VAT Central Unit (Southend-on-Sea). Since 1 April 2010, most VAT returns must be submitted online and VAT payments made electronically.

Any paper returns which are still applicable should be sent to:
HM Revenue & Customs
VAT Controller
VAT Central Unit BX5 5AT

If using a courier service to deliver returns, the Southend-on-Sea address should be used:
HM Revenue & Customs
Alexander House
21 Victoria Avenue
Southend-on-Sea SS99 1AA
Tel: 0300 200 3700

From 1 April 2012, all businesses which remain VAT-registered (including those with a turnover of less than £100,000 and which registered before 1 April 2010) will be mandated to submit their VAT return online (or authorise an agent to do so) and pay their VAT electronically.

All general enquiries should first be directed to the National Advice Service Helpline above. To obtain additional Bank Giro slips phone 0300 051 9206.

For *help with signing up for VAT Online services and submitting returns online* contact the VAT Online Services Helpdesk on 0300 200 3700 (open 8.00 am to 6.00 pm, Monday to Friday, except bank holidays). If telephoning from abroad, call: +44 2920 501 261.

A *textphone service, for customers with hearing difficulties* is available on 0300 200 3719 (temporarily unavailable due to technical problems) and a Welsh-speaking service is available on 0300 200 3705. All services are available from 8.00am to 6.00pm, Monday to Friday. Any specialist functions dealt with in a particular office are shown in brackets.

To discuss a debt contact the Debt Management Unit on 0300 200 3830. (Note: all DIY sections have been transferred to the Birmingham Office (see below).)

See also new information on money laundering regulations and the Supervised Business Register on page 126.

Email enquiries:

A registered person with a general enquiry about VAT can contact HMRC at the following email addresses. (The National Advice Service should be contacted on 0300 200 3700 to establish which is the relevant address):

Belfast	*enquiries.ni.bau@hmrc.gsi.gov.uk*
Birmingham	*enquiries.wm@hmrc.gsi.gov.uk*
Cardiff	*enquiries.wales@hmrc.gsi.gov.uk*
Glasgow	*enquiries.sco@hmrc.gsi.gov.uk*
Hove	*enquiries.se@hmrc.gsi.gov.uk*
London	*enquiries.lon@hmrc.gsi.gov.uk*
Newcastle upon Tyne	*enquiries.yhne@hmrc.gsi.gov.uk*
North West England	*enquiries.nw@hmrc.gsi.gov.uk*
Poole	*enquiries.estn@hmrc.gsi.gov.uk*
Reading	*enquiries.sec@hmrc.gsi.gov.uk*
Southend-on-Sea	*enquiries.estn@hmrc.gsi.gov.uk*

Note: This is not a secure route for sending personal/commercial information.

---

001 ABERDEEN

Ruby House
8 Ruby Place
Aberdeen AB10 1ZP

069 BEDFORD

Chailey House
26-35 Cardington Road
Bedford MK42 0YS

007 BELFAST

(Head Office, Northern Ireland)
Custom House
Custom House Square
Belfast BT1 3ET

051 BIRMINGHAM

(Head Office, Central England; includes DIY House Building Claims Unit)
City Centre House
30 Union Street
Birmingham B2 4AD

020 BLACKBURN

Centenary Court
Blackburn BB1 4DB

039 BRISTOL

(Head Office, Southern Region)
(General enquiries to National Advice Helpline)

103 CAMBRIDGE
(General enquiries to National Advice Helpline)

078 CANTERBURY
(General enquiries to National Advice Helpline)

010 CARLISLE
(Now handled by Newcastle-upon-Tyne)

023 CHESTER
(General enquiries to National Advice Helpline)

058 **CHESTERFIELD**

Markham House
112 Markham Road
Chesterfield S40 1SR
(Debt Management Unit)

104 **CITY (LONDON)**
*(General enquiries to National
Advice Helpline)*

060 **COLCHESTER**

14 Headgate
Colchester CO3 3BS
Tel: 0300 200 3830
(Debt Management Unit)

052 **COVENTRY**

Sherbourne House
1 Manor House Drive
Coventry CV1 2TA

088 **CROYDON**

Southern House
Wellesley Grove
Croydon CR9 1TR
(Debt Management Unit)

DOUGLAS
*(See the Channel Islands, Ireland and The Isle of Man
section)*

DOVER

Centurion House
Bench Street
Dover CT16 1RG
Tel: 0300 200 3700

053 **DROITWICH**
*(General enquiries to
National Advice Helpline)*

064 **DUNDEE**

Caledonian House
Greenmarket
Dundee DD1 4QX

097 **EAST LONDON
BUSINESS CENTRE**
*(General enquiries to
National Advice Helpline)*

ENNISKILLEN

Abbey House, Head Street
Enniskillen
Fermanagh BT74 7JL
*(General enquiries to
National Advice Helpline)*

031 **EXETER**
*(General enquiries to
National Advice Helpline)*

092 **FINCHLEY**

Berkeley House, 304 Regents
Park Road
London N3 2JY
*(General enquiries to
National Advice Helpline)*

005 **GLASGOW**

Cotton House
7 Cochrane Street
Glasgow G1 1HY
(Debt Management Unit)

006 **GREENOCK**

3rd Floor
99 Dalrymple Street
Greenock PA15 1QW

042 **GRIMSBY**

Imperial House
77 Victoria Street
Grimsby DN31 1DB
Tel: 0300 200 3700

015 **HALIFAX**
*(Closed. General enquiries to
National Advice Helpline)*

055 **HANLEY**

Blackburn House
Old Hall Street
Hanley ST1 3BS

084 **HARLOW**

Beaufort House
Crown Gate
Harlow CM20 1NB

016 **HULL**

Custom House
King George Dock
Hull HU9 5PW
Fax: 01482 785 971

061 **IPSWICH**

7th Floor
St Clare House
Greyfriars
Princes Street
Ipswich IP1 1LW

045 **KETTERING**
*(Closed. General enquiries to
National Advice Helpline)*

017 **LEEDS**

Peter Bennett House
Redvers Close
West Park Ring Road
Leeds LS16 6RQ

043 **LEICESTER**

Citygate House
St Margarets Way
Leicester LE1 3DA

042 **LINCOLN**
*(Closed. General enquiries to
National Advice Helpline)*

024 **LIVERPOOL**

Regian House
James Street
Liverpool L75 1AA
*(Debt Management Unit; Na-
tional Insolvency Operations;
National Civil Recovery Unit)*

069 **LUTON**

King House
George Street West
Luton LU1 2D2
*(General enquiries to National
Advice Helpline)*

081 **MAIDENHEAD**
*(Closed. General enquiries to
National Advice Helpline)*

095 **MANCHESTER**

Ralli Quays
3 Stanley Street
Salford M60 9LA
(Solicitors Office)

011 **MIDDLESBROUGH**
*(General enquiries to
National Advice Helpline)*

012 **NEWCASTLE-UPON-TYNE**

Dobson House
Regent Centre
Gosforth
Newcastle-upon-Tyne NE3 3PF
*(Centre of Expertise for Min-
eral Oils Relief; Landfill Sec-
tor Co-ordination Unit)*

NEWRY
*(Closed. General enquiries to
National Advice Helpline)*

045 **NORTHAMPTON**

Princess House
Cliftonville Road
Northampton NN1 5AE

062 **NORWICH**
*(Closed. General enquiries to
National Advice Helpline)*

032 **PLYMOUTH (LIMITED
OPERATIONS)**

Crownhill Court, Tailyour
Road
Crownhill
Plymouth PL6 5BZ

*(General enquiries to
National Advice Helpline)*

071 **POOLE**
*(General enquiries to
National Advice Helpline)*

070 **PORTSMOUTH**

2nd Floor
Wingfield House
316 Commercial Road
Portsmouth PO1 4TG
*(General telephone enquiries to
National Advice Helpline.
Written
enquiries to Southend – see be-
low – using postcode SS99
1BD)*

077 **READING**
*(Closed. General enquiries to
National Advice Helpline)*

082 **REDHILL**

Warwick House
67 Station Road
Redhill RH1 1QU
Fax: 01737 734 650

027 **SALFORD**

Custom House, Furness Quay
Salford M5 2XX

018 **SHEFFIELD**
*(Closed. General enquiries to
National Advice Helpline)*

056 **SHREWSBURY**
*(Closed. General enquiries to
National Advice Helpline)*

105 **SOUTH BANK (LONDON)**
*(Closed. General enquiries to
National Advice Helpline)*

072 **SOUTHAMPTON**

Compass House
Maybush
Romsey Road
Southampton SO16 4HP

(Debt Management Unit)

099 **SOUTHEND-ON-SEA**

Alexander House
21 Victoria Avenue
Southend-on-Sea SS99 1AA
*(Central Unit: keeps
registration records, issues and
receives return forms, receives
payments and repays VAT)*

010 **SOUTH LAKES**
*(Now handled by Newcastle-
upon-Tyne)*

101 **STAINES**

Forum House
14 Thames Street
Staines TW18 4UD

STOKE-ON-TRENT
*(Closed. General enquiries to
National Advice Helpline)*

037 **SWANSEA**

Ty-nant
180 High Street
Swansea SA1 5AP

TAUNTON
*(General enquiries to
National Advice Helpline)*

032 **TRURO**
*(Closed. General enquiries to
National Advice Helpline)*

090 **UXBRIDGE**

Valiant House
1 Park Road
Uxbridge UB8 1RW
Fax: 01895 814 401

019 **WASHINGTON**
*(General enquiries to
National Advice Helpline)*

| 091 | **WEMBLEY** | 057 | **WOLVERHAMPTON** |

091   **WEMBLEY**

Valiant House
365 High Road
Wembley HA9 6AA

029   **WIGAN**

Lingate House
102 Chapel Lane
Wigan WN3 4BJ

057   **WOLVERHAMPTON**

VAT Registration Service
Crown House
Birch Street
Wolverhampton WV1 4JX
*(General enquiries to
National Advice Helpline)*

YORK
*(General enquiries to
National Advice Helpline)*

VAT Office Tracer

Local VAT Offices are listed below in numerical order so that the Office may be traced from the official number.

001	Aberdeen	057	Wolverhampton
004	Colwyn Bay	058	Chesterfield
005	Glasgow	060	Colchester
006	Greenock	061	Ipswich
007	Belfast	062	Norwich
010	South Lakes & Carlisle	063	Edinburgh
011	Middlesbrough	064	Dundee
012	Newcastle upon Tyne	069	Bedford & Luton
015	Halifax	070	Portsmouth
016	Hull	071	Poole
017	Leeds	072	Southampton
018	Doncaster & Sheffield	073	Brighton
019	Washington	075	Oxford
020	Blackburn	077	Reading
021	Cheadle	078	Canterbury
023	Chester	079	Maidstone
024	Liverpool	081	Maidenhead
027	Salford	082	Redhill
029	Wigan	083	Woking
031	Exeter	084	Harlow
032	Plymouth & Truro	088	Croydon
035	Cardiff	090	Uxbridge
037	Swansea	091	Wembley
039	Bristol	092	Finchley
041	Derby	095	Manchester
042	Lincoln & Grimsby	097	East London Business Centre
043	Leicester	099	Southend-on-Sea
044	Nottingham	101	Staines
045	Kettering & Northampton	102	Hastings
046	Peterborough	103	Cambridge
051	Birmingham	104	City (London)
052	Coventry	105	South Bank (London)
055	Hanley		
056	Shrewsbury		

Customs – Complaints

Complaints are no longer handled by Customs. They are now handled by the UK Border Force. For full information see: *What you can do if things are seized by HMRC*, HMRC Reference: Notice 12A (September 2013).

This Notice 12A gives important advice and information about what to do if one has had something seized by HM Revenue & Customs (HMRC) or the UK Border Force. It applies to the seizure of things, such as goods and vehicles, under section 139 of the Customs and Excise Management Act 1979. It does not apply to seizures carried out under any other law.

The process is the same even though they are separate government organisations. However, there are different contact details for HMRC and the UK Border Force. It is important to contact the correct organisation, depending on who seized something, so that the case can be dealt with promptly.

For general advice or more copies of information Notices, one may phone the HMRC helpline on 0300 200 3700 between 8am and 8pm, Monday to Friday. This applies whether the goods were seized by HMRC or by the UK Border Force. A textphone service is available on 0300 200 3719. To speak to someone in Welsh, phone 0300 200 1900 between 8am and 6pm, Monday to Friday.

For items seized by the UK Border Force, for example on arrival in the UK at a port or airport or at an import postal hub, the Notice of Claim should be sent to the Border Force National Post Seizure Unit. If things were seized by HMRC, the Notice of Claim should be sent to:
HM Revenue & Customs
Specialist Investigations Appeals and Reviews Team S0777
PO Box 29992
Glasgow G70 6AB

The role of the Adjudicator remains the same: those unhappy with the outcome of dealings with a Complaints Unit may refer their case to the Adjudicator.

Border Force National Post Seizure Unit
UK Border Force
3rd Floor
West Point
Ebrington Street
Plymouth PL4 9LT
Tel: 0300 058 8703
Fax: 0300 058 8968

The Adjudicator's Office
PO Box 10280
Nottingham NG2 9PF
Tel: 0300 057 1111
Fax: 0300 059 4513
DX: 147385 Piccadilly 7
www.adjudicatorsoffice.gov.uk

Customs – Special Offices

Gambling tax changes from 1 December 2014

From 1 December 2014 HMRC is changing how gross gambling profits are taxed from 'place of supply' to 'place of consumption'. Suppliers will become liable to one or more of the taxes General Betting Duty (GBD), Pool Betting Duty (PBD) or Remote Betting Duty (RGD), if they offer remote gambling to a person who usually lives in the UK. This applies no matter where in the world they are based. UK-based operators who supply remote gambling to customers who do not usually live in the UK will no longer be liable to GBD, PBD or RGD on those transactions. HMRC now offers a Gambling Tax Online for Agents service. This will enable them to carry out a number of tasks online, including: submit tax returns for GBD, PBD and RGD and viewing liabilities and payments.

For further details see: www.gov.uk/guidance/gambling-tax-for-agents-online-service.

HMRC National Registration Unit
HM Revenue & Customs
National Registration Unit
Portcullis House
21 India Street
Glasgow G2 4PZ

Internal Audit Division
HM Revenue & Customs
9th Floor West
Alexander House
Victoria Avenue
Southend-on-Sea SS99 1AA

For postal enquiries relating to importing, exporting and customs reliefs
HM Revenue and Customs
CITEX Written Enquiry Team
Local Compliance S0000
Newcastle NE98 1ZZ

National Import Reliefs Unit
HM Revenue and Customs' (HMRC) National Import Reliefs Unit (NIRU) is the single national office responsible for the control of imports from outside the EU, where any of the following procedures and reliefs have been used:

- Inward Processing (IP) using an Authorisation by Declaration
- Community System of Duty Reliefs (CSDR)
- Outward Processing Relief (OPR) using an Authorisation by Declaration
- Returned Goods Relief (RGR)
- End-use using an Authorisation by Declaration
- Onward Supply Relief (OSR)

Further details can be found at: www.gov.uk/guidance/hmrcs-national-import-reliefs-unit-niru.
The NIRU is open from 8am to 4pm, Monday to Friday and can be contacted at:

HM Revenue and Customs
National Import Reliefs Unit (Abbey House)
Head Street
Enniskillen
Northern Ireland BT74 7JL
Tel: 03000 572100
Fax: 03000 518701
email: niru@hmrc.gsi.gov.uk

NHS VAT Helpline
HM Revenue & Customs
4th Floor
Dorset House
Stamford Street
London SE1 9PY
Tel: 0300 200 3700

Solicitor's Office
1st floor
South West Wing
Bush House, Strand
London WC2B 4RD
General Counsel & Solicitor: Gill Aitken

Statistics & Analysis of Trade Unit (SATU)
HM Revenue & Customs
Alexander House
21 Victoria Avenue
Southend-on-Sea SS99 1AA
Tel: 0300 200 3700

Tariff Classification Helpline
Following a consultation on future needs, the tariff classification helpline has been changed to an email enquiry service. These should be sent to: classification.enquiries@hmrc.gsi.gov.uk.

UKBA National Frontiers Approval Unit
National Frontier Approvals Unit

UK Border Agency
1st Floor
Admin Block
The Cargo Centre
Birmingham International Airport
Birmingham B26 3QN
email: nationalfrontierapprovals unit@homeoffice.gsi.gov.uk

VAT and Excise and Other Duties including Aggregates Levy
HM Revenue & Customs
Alexander House
21 Victoria Avenue
Southend-on-Sea SS99 1AA
email: enquiries.estn@hmrc.gsi.gov.uk

Charities Sector

Charity Commission

The Charity Commission is a government-appointed body, which is broadly responsible for the support and supervision, including the registration, of charities (except in Scotland).

Note that the decision to grant beneficial tax status is a separate matter, dealt with by HM Revenue and Customs. Historically, the two organisations would, in general, liaise and agree on any decision.

Charity Commission First Contact is the new single point of contact for all new enquiries and requests for services coming into the Commission, including to register a Charity. In the first instance, all correspondence should be sent to:
Charity Commission
PO Box: 211
Bootle L20 7YX
Tel: 0300 066 9197 (Technical support helpline)
Fax: 0151 703 1555
email: enquiries@charitycommission.gov.uk
www.charitycommission.gov.uk

See also under Agent Contacts on page 49 and the First-tier Tribunal (Charity) entry on page 108.

(London Office)
Harmsworth House
13-15 Bouverie Street
London EC4Y 8DP
www.charity-commission.gov.uk

(Taunton Office)
Woodfield House
Tangier
Taunton TA1 4BL

(Liverpool Office)
12 Princes Dock
Liverpool L 31

(Newport office)
Room 1, 364
Government Buildings
Cardiff Road
Newport NP10 8XG
Official Custodian for Charities

(Address and telephone as for Charity Commission)

Charities Advisory Trust
Radius Works
Back Lane
Hampstead
London NW3 1HL
Tel: 020 7794 9835
Fax: 020 7431 3739
email:
people@charitiesadvisorytrust.org.uk
www.charitiesadvisorytrust.co.uk

Charities Aid Foundation
25 Kings Hill Avenue
Kings Hill
West Malling ME19 4TA
Tel: 0300 012 3000
Fax: 0300 012 3001

email: enquiries@cafonline.org
www.cafonline.org

Directory of Social Change
London Office
352 Hollway Road
London N7 6PA
Tel: 08450 777 707
email: publication@dsc.org.uk
www.dsc.org.uk

Liverpool Office
Suite 103
1 Old Hall Street
Liverpool L3 9HG

National Council for Voluntary Organisations
Society Building
8 All Saints Street
London N1 9RL
Tel: 020 7520 2414
Fax: 020 7713 6300
Helpdesk: 0300 012 0179
email: ncvo@ncvo.org.uk
www.ncvo.org.uk

National Housing Federation
Lion Court
25 Procter Street
London WC1V 6NY
Tel: 020 7067 1010
Fax: 020 7067 1011
email: info@housing.org.uk
www.housing.org.uk

Northern Ireland Federation of Housing Associations
6C Citylink
Business Park
Albert Street
Belfast BT12 4HB
Tel: 028 9023 0446
Fax: 028 9023 8057
email: info@nifha.org
www.nifha.org

Registry of Friendly Societies
(Part of the Financial Conduct Authority)
25 The North Colonnade
Canary Wharf
London E14 5HS
Tel: 0300 500 0597/020 7066 1000
Fax: 020 7066 1099
email: consumer.queries@fca.org.uk or firm.queries@fca.org.uk
www.fca.org.uk

Office of Scottish Charity Regulator
The powers of the Charity Commission and the *Charities Acts* do not extend to Scotland.

Scottish Federation of Housing Associations
3rd Floor, Sutherland House
149 St Vincent Street
Glasgow G2 5NW
Tel: 0141 332 8113
Fax: 0141 332 9684
email: sfha@fsfha.co.uk
www.sfha.co.uk

Payroll Giving

HM Revenue and Customs produce various publications and a CD-ROM on the subject of Gift Aid and Payroll Giving. The following is a list of professional fundraising organisations involved in Payroll Giving.

Hands On Helping
Fairfields
117 Castleton Road
Hope
Hope Valley S33 6SB
Tel: 01433 621 882
email: info@hands-on-helping.co.uk
www.hands-on-helping.co.uk

Payroll Giving in Action Ltd
Millennium House
Brannam Crescent
Barnstaple
Devon EX31 3TD
Tel: 01271 344 360
email: enquiry@payrollgiving.co.uk
www.payrollgiving.com

Payroll Giving In Action Ltd Northern Ireland
32 Hamilton Road
Bangor
County Down BT20 4LE
Tel: 02891 859 561
Fax: 02891 859 562

Sharing the Caring
Fernleigh
Bullockstone Road
Herne
Kent CT6 7NL
Tel: 01227 361 960
Fax: 01227 369 281
email: enquiries@stcpayrollgiving.co.uk
www.stcpayrollgiving.co.uk

Business Directory

Companies House

Companies House is an executive office of the Department for Business, Innovation and Skills, performing three basic roles:

* incorporation and dissolving limited companies;
* examining and storing company information delivered under the Companies Act and related legislation; and
* making this information available to the public.

The various Companies House offices and facilities are listed below.

HEAD OFFICE

Companies House
Crown Way
Cardiff CF14 3UZ
Tel: 0303 1234 500
Minicom: 02920 381 245
(number for all offices)
DX 33050 Cardiff
email: enquiries@companies-house.gov.uk
www.companieshouse.gov.uk
(Head office for England and Wales, providing all services, including general enquiries.)

Companies House
4 Abbey Orchard Street
Westminster
London SW1P 2HT
Tel: 0303 1234 500
(Company search and document filing facilities.)

SCOTLAND

Head Office
4th Floor
Edinburgh Quay 2
139 Fountainbridge
Edinburgh EH3 9FF
LP-4 Edinburgh 2 (Legal Post) or DX ED 235 Edinburgh 1
(Head office for Scotland, providing all services.)

NORTHERN IRELAND

Companies House
2nd Floor
The Linenhall
32–38 Linenhall Street
Belfast BT2 8BG
DX 481 N.R. Belfast 1
(Head office for NI, providing all services.)

Consumer Protection

Information Commissioner's Office
Wycliffe House
Water Lane
Wilmslow SK9 5AF
Helpline: 0303 123 1113
Notification Line: 01625 545 740
Data Protection Help: 01625 545 745
Switchboard: 01625 545 700
Fax: 01625 524 510
email: registration@ico.org.uk
or casework@ico.org.uk (please include you telephone number) www.ico.org.uk
The Registrar is required by the *Data Protection Act 1994* to establish and maintain a register of data users and computer bureaux. The *Act* requires registration of all users and bureaux holding personal data, or providing personal data services. The Registrar has the power not only to serve various notices, but also to enter premises and seize material, in order to enforce the provisions of the *Act*.

Office of Fair Trading
The Office of Fair Trading closed on 31 March 2014, and its work and responsibilities passed to a number of different bodies. For details see the archived page at http://webarchive.nationalarchives.gov.uk/20140402142426/http://www.oft.gov.uk/about-the-oft/work-and-responsibilities.

Competition and Markets Authority
Victoria House
37 Southampton Row
London
WC1B 4AD
Email: general.enquiries@cma.gsi.gov.uk
Tel: 020 3738 6000
The Competition and Markets Authority (CMA) was set up in October 2013 under the Enterprise and Regulatory Reform Act 2013 and brings together the Competition Commission and the competition and certain consumer functions of the former Office of Fair Trading in a single body.

Financial Conduct Authority
25 The North Colonnade
Canary Wharf
London E14 5HS
Tel (General): 020 7066 1000
Consumer Helpline: 0800 111 6768
Firm Helpline: 0300 500 0597
email: consumer.queries@fca.org.uk
www.fca.org.uk
The Financial Conduct Authority regulates the financial services industry and consumer credit industry in the UK. It has rule-making, investigative and enforcement powers to protect and regulate the financial services industry. The new organisation takes over part of the role of the former Financial Services Authority, which it shares with the Prudential Regulation Authority.

Prudential Regulation Authority (PRA)
Bank of England
Threadneedle Street
London EC2R 8AH
Tel: 020 7601 4878
Email: enquiries@bankofengland.co.uk
For enquiries from firms contact:

Firms Enquiries Team (MG1-SE)
Prudential Regulation Authority
20 Moorgate
London EC2R 6DA
Tel: 020 3461 7000
Email:
pra.firmenquiries@bankofengland.co.uk
The Prudential Regulation Authority (PRA) became responsible for the prudential regulation and supervision of banks, building societies, credit unions, insurers and major investment firms on 1 April 2013. It regulates around 1,700 financial firms.
The PRA was created by the *Financial Services Act 2012* and is part of the

Bank of England. It has close working relationships with other parts of the Bank, including the Financial Policy Committee and the Special Resolution Unit. The PRA also works alongside the Financial Conduct Authority, creating a 'twin peaks' regulatory structure in the UK.

Financial Services Compensation Scheme
10th floor
Beaufort House
15 St Botolph Street
London EC3A 7QU
Tel: 0800 678 1100 / 020 7741 4100
The Financial Services Compensation Scheme (FSCS) is the UK's compensation fund of last resort for customers of authorised financial services firms. They may pay compensation if a firm is unable, or likely to be unable, to pay claims against it. This is usually because it has stopped trading or has been declared in default.
The FSCS covers business conducted by firms authorised by the Financial Conduct Authority, the independent watchdog set up by government to regulate financial services in the UK and protect the rights of consumers.

The Court Service
102 Petty France
London SW1H 9AJ
Tel: 020 3334 3555
email: generalenquiries@justice.gsi.gov.uk
www.justice.gov.uk
The County Court procedure for small claims enables private individuals, without legal experience, to make or defend claims for less than £5,000 in an informal atmosphere and without the risk of having to pay legal costs should they lose.
The main types of small claim brought are for debt recovery, consumer claims and actions by small businesses for breach of contract. Proceedings are usually initiated by contacting your local County Court.

PUBLIC UTILITIES' REGULATORS

OFCOM (Office of Telecommunications)
Riverside House
2A Southwark Bridge Road
London SE1 9HA
Tel: 020 7981 3000
Fax: 020 7981 3333
Textphone: 020 7981 3043
email: contact@ofcom.org.uk
www.ofcom.org.uk

OFGEM (The Office of Gas and Electricity Market)
Head Office
9 Millbank
Millbank
London SW1P 3GE
Tel: 020 7901 7000
Fax: 020 7901 7066
www.ofgem.gov.uk

ORR (The Office of Rail and Road)
1 Kemble Street
London WC2B 4AN
Tel: 020 7282 2000
Fax: 020 7282 2040
email: contact.cct@orr.gsi.gov.uk
www.orr.gov.uk

OFWAT (The Office of Water Services)
Centre City Tower
7 Hill Street
Birmingham B5 4UA
Tel: 0121 644 7500
Fax: 0121 644 7559
Minicom: 0121 625 1422
email: mailbox@ofwat.gsi.gov.uk
www.ofwat.gov.uk

INDEPENDENT COMPLAINTS SCHEMES AND FINANCIAL OMBUDSMEN
Independent complaints schemes aim to settle disputes about financial products or services impartially and services are free for consumers.
They can help when individuals have not been able to resolve the complaint using the relevant internal complaints procedure.

Financial Ombudsman Service
Exchange Tower
London E14 9SR
Tel: 020 7964 1000
Consumer helpline: 0800 023 4567 /
0300 123 9123
(Monday to Friday, 8.30am—8.00pm,
Saturday 9.00am to 1.00pm)
Fax: 020 7964 1001
email: complaint.info@financial-
ombudsman.org.uk
www.financial-ombudsman.org.uk

**Finance & Leasing Association
Arbitration Scheme**
Finance & Leasing Association
2nd Floor
Imperial House
15-19 Kingsway
London WC2B 6UN
Tel: 020 7836 6511
Fax: 020 7420 9600
email: info@fla.org.uk

The Pensions Advisory Service (TPAS)
TPAS provides guidance on most types
of pensions and helps members of the
public who have problems or complaints
with their occupational or private pension.
11 Belgrave Road
London SW1V 1RB
National helpline: 0300 123 1047
Helpline for women: 0345 600 0806
Helpline for self-employed: 0345 602
7021
Fax: 020 7592 7000
email:
enquiries@pensionsadvisoryservice.org.uk
www.pensionsadvisoryservice.org.uk

The Pensions Ombudsman
The Pensions Ombudsman is also the
Pension Protection Fund Chairman
The Office of the Pensions Ombudsman
11 Belgrave Road
London SW1V 1RB
Tel: 020 7630 2200
Fax: 020 7821 0065
email: enquiries@pensions-
ombudsman.org.uk
www.pensions-ombudsman.org.uk

OTHER USEFUL ADDRESSES

Advertising Standards Authority
Mid City Place

71 High Holborn
London WC1V 6QT
Tel: 020 7492 2222
Fax: 020 7242 3696
email: enquiries@asa.org.uk
www.asa.org.uk

British Standards Institution (BSI)
389 Chiswick High Road
London W4 4AL
Tel: 020 8996 9000
Fax: 020 8996 7001
email: cservices@bsigroup.com
www.bsigroup.com

Consumer Focus
Consumer Focus has now changed
to Consumer Futures. Functions are
now dealt with by Citizens Advice, Citizens Advice Scotland and the Consumer Council for Northern Ireland. For
further information see
www.citizensadvice.org.uk/consumer,
www.cas.org.uk and
www.consumercouncil.org.uk.

Intellectual Property Office
(formerly the Patent Office)
Head Office
Concept House
Cardiff Road
Newport NP10 8QQ
Tel: 0300 300 2000
Fax: 01633 817 777
Minicom (text phone): 0300 020 0015
email: information@ipo.gov.uk
www.ipo.gov.uk

London Office
The Patent Office
4 Abbey Orchard Street
London SW1P 2HT

**Local Authorities' Coordinators of
Regulatory Services (LACORS)**
Local Government House
Smith Square
London SW1P 3HZ
Tel: 020 7664 3000
Fax: 020 7664 3030
email: info@lacors.gov.uk

**National Association of Citizens Advice
Bureaux**
3rd Floor North
200 Aldersgate Street
London EC1A 4HD

Business Directory

Tel: 0300 023 1231 (admin only)
www.citizensadvice.org.uk

National Computing Centre
1st floor Venture House
6 Silver Court
Watchmead
Welwyn Garden City
Hertfordshire AL7 1TS
Tel: 0870 908 8767
Fax: 0870 134 0931
email: info@ncc.co.uk
www.ncc.co.uk

Postwatch
*(Now part of Consumer Futures, which
has been taken over by Citizens Advice.
See above.)*

Registry Trust Limited
153–157 Cleveland Street
London W1T 6QW
Tel: 020 7380 0133
Fax: 020 7388 0672
DX 134211 Tottenham Court Road 2
email: info@trustonline.org.uk
www.trustonline.org.uk
The Registry Trust Limited register
all County Court judgments and carry
out a public search service.

Employee Interest Groups

Advisory, Conciliation and Arbitration Service (ACAS)
Euston Tower
286 Euston Road
London NW1 3JJ
Tel Helpline: 0300 123 1100
www.acas.org.uk
ACAS is a statutory body whose duties are to promote the improvement of industrial relations, particularly in the settlement of trade disputes. The service is so constituted as to maintain a balance between employers' and employees' interests. Specific enquiries, requests for leaflets etc should be directed to the nearest regional office.

Equality and Human Rights Commission
England
Equality Advisory Support Service (EASS)
Freepost Equality Advisory Support Service
FPN 4431
Opening hours:
Mon-Fri 9.00am–8.00pm
Sat 10.00am–2.00pm
Tel: 0808 800 0082
Textphone: 0808 800 0084
email: info@equalityhumanrights.com
www.equalityhumanrights.com

Wales
Block 1, Spur D
Government Buildings
St Agnes Road, Gabalfa
Cardiff CF14 4YJ
Tel: 0292 044 7710
(Non-helpline calls only)
Textphone: 0292 044 7713
Fax: 0292 044 7712
email: wales@equalityhumanrights.com

Scotland
151 West George Street
Glasgow G2 2JJ
Tel: 0141 228 5910

(Non-helpline calls only)
Fax: 0141 228 5912
email:
scotland@equalityhumanrights.com
Please note, the telephone numbers of the main offices of the Equality and Human Rights Commission are not for the helpline. Please contact the Equality Advisory Support Service if you need advice or information.

Health and Safety Executive (HSE)
Head Office:
Redgrave Court
Merton Road
Bootle
Merseyside L20 7HS
www.hse.gov.uk

Construction Division:
Rose Court
2 Southwark Bridge
London SE1 9HS
Tel: 020 7556 2100
Fax: 020 7556 2109
The *Health and Safety at Work Act 1974* established the Health and Safety Commission and the Executive, the former to advise on and the latter to implement its provisions, with the aim of securing the health, safety and welfare of people at work. The HSE and local authorities are responsible for enforcing the *Act*. They may appoint inspectors to investigate any contravention and issue improvement or prohibition notices as appropriate. The HSE also publishes many explanatory guides.

Employment Tribunals (Field Support Unit)
England and Wales
1st Floor, 100 Southgate Street
Bury St Edmunds IP33 2AQ
Tel: 0300 123 1024
Textphone: 01509 221564
email: buryet@tribunals.gsi.gov.uk
www.employmenttribunals.gov.uk

All applications to the Employment Tribunals in England and Wales should be sent to one of the regional Tribunal Offices. Each regional Office is responsible for a range of postcode areas within its region. Applications to the Tribunal about a particular organisation or employer should be sent to the regional Office dealing with the postcode area in which the organisation is based. The Employment Tribunal Enquiry Line (Tel: 0300 123 1024; Textphone: 01509 221564) will advise on the correct office. In Scotland and Northern Ireland, applications should go to the addresses below.

Scotland
Eagle Building
215 Bothwell Street
Glasgow G2 7TS
Tel: 0141 204 0730
Fax: 01264 785 177
email: glasgowet@tribunals.gsi.gov.uk
www.employmenttribunals.gov.uk

Northern Ireland
Industrial Tribunals and Fair Employment Tribunal, Northern Ireland
Killymeal House
2 Cromac Quay
Ormeau Road
Belfast BT7 2JD
Tel: 028 9032 7666
Fax: 028 9025 0100
email: mail@employmenttribunalsni.org
www.employmenttribunalsni.co.uk

Labour Research Department (LRD)
78 Blackfriars Road
London SE1 8HF
Tel: 020 7928 3649
Fax: 020 7902 9815
email: info@lrd.org.uk
www.lrd.org.uk
An independent, trade union based research organisation supplying the trade union movement, employers and individuals with quality information and publications on employment issues.

Disability Rights UK
Ground Floor, CAN Mezzanine
49–51 East Road

London N1 6AH
Tel: 020 7250 8181 (General enquiries – not an advice line)
email: enquiries@disabilityrightsuk.org
www.disabilityrightsuk.org.uk
Disability Rights UK coordinates groups working to improve the rights of people with disabilities. It can put employers and employees in touch with organisations advising on disability and employment issues.

British Safety Council (BSC)
70 Chancellor's Road
Hammersmith
London W6 9RS
Tel: 020 3510 8355
Fax: 0844 583 4731
email: mail@britsafe.org
www.britsafe.org

Certification Office for Trade Unions and Employers' Associations
22nd Floor
Euston Tower
286 Euston Road
London NW1 3JJ
Tel: 020 7210 3734
Fax: 020 7210 3612
email: info@certoffice.org
www.certoffice.org

Central Arbitration Committee (CAC)
22nd Floor
Euston Tower
286 Euston Road
London NW1 3JJ
Tel: 020 7904 2315
Fax: 020 7904 2301
email: enquiries@cac.gov.uk
www.cac.gov.uk

Centre for Effective Dispute Resolution (CEDR)
70 Fleet Street
London EC4Y 1EU
Tel: 020 7536 6000
Fax: 020 7536 6001
email: info@cedr.co.uk
www.cedr.co.uk

Construction Industry Advisory Committee (CONIAC)
The Secretary

HSE
Floor 1 SW
Rose Court
2 Southwark Bridge
London SE1 9HS
Tel: 020 7556 2191
Fax: 020 7556 2209

Department for Education
Sanctuary Buildings
Great Smith Street
London SW1P 3BT
Tel: 0370 000 2288
www.education.gov.uk

Industrial Injuries Advisory Council (IIAC)
2nd Floor
Caxton House
Tothill Street
London SW1 9NA
Tel: 020 7449 5618
email: iiac@dwp.gsi.gov.uk
www.iiac.org.uk

Institute of Employment Rights (IER)
Jack Jones House
4th Floor
1 Islington
Liverpool L3 8EG
Tel: 0151 207 5265
Fax: 0151 207 5264
email: office@ier.org.uk
www.ier.org.uk

Irish Congress of Trade Unions (NI)
Carlin House
4–6 Donegall Street Place
Belfast BT1 2FN
Tel: 028 9024 7940
Fax: 028 9024 6898
email: info@ictuni.org
www.ictuni.org

London Court of International Arbitration International Dispute Resolution Centre
70 Fleet Street
London EC4Y 1EU
Tel: 020 7936 6200
Fax: 020 7936 6211
email: lcia@lcia.org
www.lcia.org

Pensions Advisory Service
11 Belgrave Road
London SW1V 1RB
Tel: 0300 123 1047
Fax: 0207 592 7000
email:
enquiries@pensionadvisoryservice.org.uk
www.pensionsadvisoryservice.org.uk

Pension Protection Fund
Renaissance
12 Dingwall Road
Croydon CR0 2NA
Tel: 0345 600 2541/020 8633 4900
Textphone: 0845 600 2542
Fax: 0208 633 4910
email: information@ppf.gsi.gov.uk
www.pensionprotectionfund.org.uk

Public and Commercial Services Union (PCS)
PCS Head Office
160 Falcon Road
London SW11 2LN
Tel: 020 7924 2727
Fax: 020 7924 1847
www.pcs.org.uk

Scottish Trades Union Congress (STUC)
333 Woodlands Road
Glasgow G3 6NG
Tel: 0141 337 8100
Fax: 0141 337 8101
email: info@stuc.org.uk
www.stuc.org.uk

Trades Union Congress (TUC)
Congress House
23–28 Great Russell Street
London WC1B 3LS
Tel: 020 7636 4030
Fax: 020 7636 0632
email: info@tuc.org.uk
www.tuc.org.uk

Wales Trades Union Council (WTUC)
1 Cathedral Road
Cardiff CF11 9SD
Tel: 029 2034 7010
Fax: 029 2022 1940
email: wtuc@tuc.org.uk
www.wtuc.org.uk

Business Directory

Government Offices

Department for Business, Energy and Industrial Strategy
(formerly BIS)
Ministerial Correspondence Unit
1 Victoria Street
London SW1H 0ET
Tel: 020 7215 5000
Fax: 020 7215 0105
www.gov.uk/government/organisations/d
epartment-for-business-energy-and-indust
rial-strategy

Department for Work and Pensions
Caxton House
Tothill Street
London SW1H 9DA
www.dwp.gov.uk

HM Central Land Registry
Headquarters
Trafalgar House
1 Bedford Park
Croydon CR0 2AQ
Tel: 0300 006 0004
Fax: 0300 006 0024
email: hmlr@landreg.gov.uk
www.landregistry.gov.uk

HM Treasury
Correspondence & Enquiries Unit, 2/W1
HM Treasury
1 Horse Guards Road
London SW1A 2HQ
Tel: 020 7270 5000
email: public.enquiries@hm-
treasury.gov.uk
www.hm-treasury.gov.uk

Law Commission for England and Wales
1st Floor, Tower
52 Queen Anne's Gate
London SW1H 4AG
Tel: 020 3334 0200
Fax: 020 3334 0201
www.lawcom.gov.uk

Legal Services Commission
Corporate Legal Team

102 Petty France
London SW1H 9AJ
Tel: 0300 200 2020
DX 328 London
www.legalservices.gov.uk

Ministry of Justice
(formerly Department for Constitutional Affairs)
Ministry of Justice
102 Petty France
London SW1H 9AJ
Tel: 020 3334 3555
DX 152380 Westminster 8
email: general.queries@justice.gsi.gov.uk
www.justice.gov.uk

National Audit Office
157–197 Buckingham Palace Road
Victoria
London SW1W 9SP
Tel: 020 7798 7000
Fax: 020 7798 7070
email: enquiries@nao.gsi.gov.uk
www.nao.org.uk

National Crime Agency
Units 1–6
Citadel Place
Tinworth Street
London SE11 5EF
Tel: 0370 496 7622
www.nationalcrimeagency.gov.uk

Office for Budget Responsibility
Correspondence and Enquiry Unit
14T,102 Petty France
London SW1H 9AJ
Tel: 0203 334 6337
email: obrenquiries@obr.gsi.gov.uk
The Office for Budget Responsibility was formed in May 2010 to make an independent assessment of the public finances and the economy for each Budget and Pre-Budget Report.

Office for National Statistics
Government Buildings

Room 1.01
Cardiff Road
Newport NP10 8XG
Tel: 0845 601 3034
Fax: 01633 652 747
email: info@ons.gsi.gov.uk
www.ons.gov.uk

Serious Fraud Office
2–4 Cockspur Street
London SW1Y 5BS
Tel: 020 7239 7272 (switchboard)
Fax: 020 7084 4700
email: public.enquiries@sfo.gov.uk
www.sfo.gov.uk

The Scottish Executive
St Andrews House
Regent Road
Edinburgh EH1 3DG
Tel: 0300 244 4000
email: ceu@scotland.gsi.gov.uk
www.scotland.gov.uk

Professional Organisations

Accounting Standards Board (ASB)
The functions of the Accounting Standards Board are now subsumed in the Financial Reporting Council (see page 162).

Association of Accounting Technicians (AAT)
140 Aldersgate Street
London EC1A 4HY
Tel: 020 3735 2468
Fax: 020 7397 3009
email: aat@aat.org.uk
www.aat.org.uk

Association of Authorised Public Accountants (AAPA)
29 Lincoln's Inn Fields
London WC2A 3BP
Tel: 020 7059 5000
Fax: 020 7059 5916
email: info@accaglobal.com
www.accaglobal.com/aapa

Association of British Insurers (ABI)
One America Square
17 Crosswell
London EC3N 2LB
Tel: 020 7600 3333
email: info@abi.org.uk
www.abi.org.uk

Association of Chartered Certified Accountants (ACCA)
The Adelphi
1–11 John Adam Street
London WC2N 6AU
Tel: 020 7059 5000
Fax: 020 7059 5050
email: info@accaglobal.com
www.accaglobal.com

Association of Consulting Actuaries (ACA)
Regis House
First Floor
45 King William Street
London EC4R 9AN

Tel: 020 3102 6761
email: acahelp@aca.org.uk
www.aca.org.uk

Association of Corporate Treasurers (ACT)
68 King William Street
London EC4N 7DZ
Tel: 020 7847 2540
Fax: 020 7847 2598
email: enquiries@treasurers.org
www.treasurers.org

Association of Revenue and Customs (part of the First Division Association)
8 Leake Street
London SE1 7NN
Tel: 020 7401 5555
email: info@fda.org.uk
www.fda.org.uk

Association of Independent Professionals and the Self-Employed (IPSE)
Heron House
10 Dean Farrar Street
London SW1H 0DX
Tel: 020 8897 9970
Fax: 020 8759 1946
email: admin@pcg.org.uk
www.pcg.org.uk

Association of International Accountants
Staithes Three
The Watermark
Metro Riverside
Newcastle upon Tyne NE11 9SN
Tel: 0191 493 0277
Fax: 0191 493 0278
email:aia@aiaworldwide.com
www.aiaworldwide.com

Association of Taxation Technicians (ATT)
1st Floor
Artillery House
11–19 Artillery Row
London SW1P 1RT

Tel: 020 7340 0551
Fax: 020 7340 0598
email: info@att.org.uk
www.att.org.uk

Auditing Practices Board (APB)
The functions of the Accounting Standards Board are now subsumed in the Financial Reporting Council (see page 162).

UK Business Angels Association
5th Floor East
Chancery House
53–64 Chancery Lane
London WC2A 1QS
Tel: 020 7492 0490
email:
info@ukbusinessangelsassociation.org.uk
www.ukbusinessangelsassociation.org.uk

Chartered Accountants Institute of Ethics Advisory Services
Metropolitan House
321 Avebury Boulevard
Milton Keynes MK9 2FZ
Tel: 01908 248 100
email: ethics@icaew.co.uk
www.icaew.com

Chartered Institute of Arbitrators (CIARB)
12 Bloomsbury Square
London WC1A 2LP
Tel: 020 7421 7444
Fax: 020 7900 2917
email: info@ciarb.org
www.ciarb.org

Chartered Institute of Building (CIOB)
1 Arlington Square
Downshire Way
Bracknell RG12 1WA
Tel: 01344 630 700
Fax: 01344 306 430
email: reception@ciob.org.uk
www.ciob.org.uk

Chartered Institute of Loss Adjusters
20 Ironmonger Lane
London EC2V 8EP
Tel: 020 3861 5720

email: info@cila.co.uk
www.cila.co.uk

Chartered Institute of Management Accountants (CIMA)
The Helicon
One South Place
London EC2M 2RB
Tel: 020 8849 2251
email: cima.contact@cimaglobal.com
www.cimaglobal.com

Chartered Institute of Public Finance and Accountancy (CIPFA)
77 Mansell Street
London E1 8AN
Tel: 020 7543 5600
Fax: 020 7543 5700
www.cipfa.org

Chartered Institute of Taxation (CIOT)
First Floor
Artillery House
11–19 Artillery Row
London SW1P 1RT
Tel: 020 7340 0550
email: post@ciot.org.uk
www.tax.org.uk

Chartered Insurance Institute (CII)
42–48 High Road
South Woodford
London E18 2JP
Tel: 020 8989 8464
Fax: 020 8530 3052
email: customer.serv@cii.co.uk
www.cii.co.uk
or

20 Aldermanbury
London EC2V 7HY
Tel: 020 7417 4415 (Library)

Expert Witness Institute (EWI)
159–161 Temple Chambers
3–7 Temple Avenue
London EC4Y 0DA
Tel: 020 7936 2213
email: info@ewi.org.uk
www.ewi.org.uk

Financial Reporting Council (FRC)
8th Floor

125 London Wall
London EC2Y 5AS
Tel: 020 7492 2300
Fax: 020 7492 2301
www.frc.org.uk
The Financial Reporting Council has a Codes and Standards Committee to which the Accounting Council and Audit and Assurance Council feed in, replacing the ASB and APB.

Freight Transport Association Limited (FTA)
Hermes House
St Johns Road
Tunbridge Wells TN4 9UZ
Tel: 01892 526 171
Fax: 01892 534 989
email: enquiries@fta.co.uk
www.fta.co.uk

The Institute for Fiscal Studies
3rd Floor
7 Ridgmount Street
London WC1E 7AE
Tel: 020 7291 4800
Fax: 020 7323 4780
email: mailbox@ifs.org.uk
www.ifs.org.uk

Institute of Actuaries
7th Floor, Holborn Gate
High Holborn
London WC1V 7PP
Tel: 020 7632 2100
Fax: 020 7632 2111
email: institute@actuaries.org.uk
www.actuaries.org.uk

Institute of Certified Practising Accountants
Imperial House
1a Standen Avenue
Hornchurch
Essex RM12 6AA
Tel: 0800 074 2896
Fax: 01708 453 123
email: info@icpa.org.uk
www.icpa.org.uk

Institute of Certified Public Accountants in Ireland (ICPA)
17 Harcourt Street
Dublin 2

Tel: 00353 14 251000
Fax: 00353 14 251001
email: cpa@cpaireland.ie
www.cpaireland.ie

Institute of Chartered Accountants in England & Wales (ICAEW)
Chartered Accountants' Hall
Moorgate Place
London EC2R 6EA
Tel (general): 020 7920 8100
Fax (general): 020 7920 0547
Tel (Tax Faculty): 020 7920 8646
email: taxfac@icaew.com
www.icaew.co.uk

Institute of Chartered Accountants in Ireland (ICAI)
Chartered Accountants House
32–38 Linenhall Street
Belfast BT2 8BG
Tel: 028 904 35840
Fax: 028 9023 0071
email: ca@icai.ie
www.icai.ie

Institute of Chartered Accountants of Scotland (ICAS)
CA House
21 Haymarket Yards
Edinburgh EH12 5BH
Tel: 0131 347 0100
Fax: 0131 347 0105
email: enquiries@icas.org.uk
www.icas.org.uk

Institute of Chartered Secretaries and Administrators (ICSA)
Saffron House
6–10 Kirby Street
London EC1N 8TS
Tel: 020 7580 4741
Fax: 020 7323 1132
email: info@icsa.co.uk
www.icsa.org.uk

Institute of Credit Management (ICM)
The Water Mill
Station Road
South Luffenham
Oakham LE15 8NB
Tel: 01780 722 900
Fax: 01780 721 333

email: info@cicm.com
www.cicm.com

Institute of Export (IE)
Export House
Minerva Business Park
Lynch Wood
Peterborough PE2 6FT
Tel: 01733 404 400
Fax: 01733 404 444
email: institute@export.org.uk
www.export.org.uk

Institute of Financial Accountants (IFA)
The Podium
1 Eversholt Street
Euston
London NW1 2DN
Tel: 020 7554 0730
email: mail@ifa.org.uk
www.ifa.org.uk

Institute of Indirect Taxation
Now merged with the Chartered Institute of Taxation (CIOT) (see page 162).

Institute of Risk Management (IRM)
2nd Floor
Sackville House
143-149 Fenchurch St
London EC3M 6BN
Tel: 020 7709 9808
Fax: 020 7709 0716
email: enquiries@theirm.org
www.theirm.org

Institute of Trade Mark Attorneys (ITMA)
5th Floor
Outer Temple
222–225 Strand
London WC2R 1BA
Tel: 020 7101 6090
Fax: 020 7101 6099
email: tm@itma.org.uk
www.itma.org.uk

International Accounting Standards Board (IASB)
1st Floor
30 Cannon Street
London EC4M 6XH

Tel: 020 7246 6410
Fax: 020 7246 6411
email: info@ifrs.org
www.ifrs.org

International Association of Book-Keepers (IAB)
Suite 5
20 Churchill Square
Kings Hill
West Malling ME19 4YU
Tel: 01732 897750
Fax: 01732 897751
email: mail@iab.org.uk
www.iab.org.uk

International Chamber of Commerce (ICC United Kingdom)
1st Floor
1–3 Staple Inn
London WC1V 7QH
Tel: 020 7838 9363
email: info@iccwbo.uk
www.iccwbo.uk

International Chamber of Shipping (ICS)
38 St Mary Axe
London EC3A 8BH
Tel: 020 7090 1460
Fax: 020 7090 1484
email: info@ics-shipping.org

International Shipping Federation
(Address as for ICS)
Tel: 020 7090 1460
Fax: 020 7090 1484
email: info@ics-shipping.org

Law Society
113 Chancery Lane
London WC2A 1PL
Tel: 020 7242 1222
Fax: 020 7831 0344
email: info.services@lawsociety.org.uk
www.lawsociety.org.uk

Law Society of Scotland
Atria One
144 Morrison Street
Edinburgh EH3 8EX
Tel: 0131 226 7411
Fax: 0131 225 2934

email: lawscot@lawscot.org.uk
www.lawscot.org.uk

Pensions and Lifetime Savings Association (PLSA)
Cheapside House
138 Cheapside
London EC2V 6AE
Tel: 020 7601 1700
email: plsa@plsa.co.uk
www.plsa.co.uk

Pensions Management Institute (PMI)
PMI House
4–10 Artillery Lane
London E1 7LS
Tel: 020 7247 1452
Fax: 020 7375 0603
email: enquiries@pensions-pmi.org.uk
www.pensions-pmi.org.uk

Royal Institute of British Architects (RIBA)
66 Portland Place
London W1B 1AD
Tel: 020 7580 5533
Fax: 020 7255 1541
www.architecture.com

Royal Institution of Chartered Surveyors (RICS)
12 Great George Street
Parliament Square
London SW1P 3AD
Tel: 024 7686 8555
Fax: 020 7334 3811
www.rics.org

(For general enquiries)

Society of Trust and Estate Practitioners (STEP)
Artillery House (South)
11–19 Artillery Row
London SW1P 1RT
Tel: 020 3752 3700
email: step@step.org
www.step.org

Tax Aid
Studio 304
The Print Rooms
164–180 Union Street
London SE1 0LH
Tel: 020 7803 4950
Helpline: 0345 120 3779
email: contact@taxaid.org.uk
www.taxaid.org.uk

The Academy of Experts (TAE)
3 Gray's Inn Square
London WC1R 5AH
Tel: 020 7430 0333
Fax: 020 7430 0666
email: admin@academy-experts.org
www.academyofexperts.org

VAT Practitioners Group (VPG)
105 Oxhey Avenue
Watford WD19 4HB
Tel: 01923 230 788
email: info@vpgweb.com
www.vpgweb.com

Business Directory

Helplines

HMRC — Revenue

Bereavement Helpline		0300 200 3300
BillPay plus		0300 200 3601
Blind Person's Helpline		0300 200 3301
Business Payment Support Service		0300 200 3835

Charities Helpline (Mon–Fri, 8.30am–4.30pm)

HMRC Charities (Bootle)	Telephone	0300 123 1073
	Telephone form requests	0300 123 1073

Child Benefit Helpline		0300 200 3100
Collection Field Force Verification Helpline		0300 200 3862

Construction Industry Scheme

Construction Industry Scheme Helpline		0300 200 3210
Calling from overseas:	Tel (with International code)	44 161 930 8706

Corporation Tax Self Assessment

Corporation Tax Helpline		0300 200 3410
Corporation Tax form ordering		0300 200 3411
		Fax: 0300 200 3419
Calling from overseas:	Tel (with International code)	44 151 268 0571

Deceased Estates Helpline

General advice and information about Income Tax and Capital Gains Tax on deceased estates. For specific enquiries telephone the relevant tax office.
(Mon-Fri, 9.00am–5.00pm)

0300 123 1072

Debt Management Helpline	0300 200 3887

Employer's Helplines (open Mon–Fri, 8.00am–8.00pm; Sat, 8.00am–4.00pm)

New Employers	0300 200 3211
	Textphone: 0300 200 3212
	Fax: 0300 052 3030
Existing Employers	0300 200 3200
	Fax: 0300 052 3030

Orderline	0300 123 1074

Flooding Helpline (open Mon–Fri, 8.00am–8.00pm, weekends 8.00am–4.00pm. Closed bank holidays)   0345 988 1188

The helpline is intended for anyone affected by flooding to get fast practical help and advice on a wide range of tax problems they may be facing.

Guardian's Allowance Helpline   0300 200 3101

HMRC Residency (Mon–Fri, 8.00am–5.00pm)

Income tax/capital gains tax enquiries	Tel: 0300 200 3300
Charity, Assets and Residents Helpline	Tel: 0300 200 3300
National Insurance contributions enquiries for non-UK residents	Tel: 0300 200 3500
Calling from overseas: Tel (with International code)	44 191 203 7010
Non-Resident Landlords Helpline	Tel: 44 3000 516 644
	Website: www.hmrc.gov.uk/international/nr-landlords.htm
Non-Resident Payment Helpline	Tel: +44 (0) 300 053 8802

IR 35 Helpline   0300 123 2326

Individual Savings Accounts Helpline
(Mon–Fri, 8.30am–4.30pm)   0300 200 3312

Inheritance Tax and Probate Helpline   0300 123 1072

Jobcentre Plus Tax Evasion Hotline (Mon–Fri, 8.00am–6.00pm)   0800 854 440

Newly Self-Employed Helpline
(Mon–Fri, 8.00am–8.00pm; Sat-Sun 8.00am-4.00pm)   0300 200 3500
0845 915 3296 (Textphone)

Online Debit and Credit Card Payments — BillPay Helpline

For help with BillPay error messages and to trace and confirm on line debit and credit card payments. Payments not taken over the phone. (Mon–Fri, 8.00am to 5.00pm)   0300 200 3601

Online Services Helpdesk   0300 200 3600
(Mon–Fri, 8.00am–8.00pm; Sat–Sun, 8.00am–10.00pm)

0300 200 3603 (Text phone)

Email: helpdesk@ir-efile.gov.uk

Pay and Work Rights Helpline (Mon–Fri, 8.00am–8.00pm; Sat 9.00am–1pm)	0300 123 1100
Payment Enquiry Helpline Please note payments cannot be made on this line	0300 200 3401
Probate and Inheritence Tax Helpline	0300 123 1072
Retirement Annuity Contracts Helplines	0300 200 3302
Savings Helpline (Mon–Fri, 8.00am–8.00pm/Sat 8.00am–4.00pm)	0300 200 3310

Self-Assessment Helpline (Mon–Sun, 8.00am–8.00pm/Sat 8.00am–4.00pm)   0300 200 3310

Calling from overseas:	Tel (with International code)	44 161 931 9070

Self-Assessment Orderline (Mon–Sun, 8.00am–8.00pm/Sat 8.00am–4.00pm)   0300 200 3610

	Fax:	0300 200 3611
Calling from overseas:	Tel (with International code)	44 161 930 8331

Self-Assessment Payment Helpline	0300 200 3822
Self-Employed Contact Centre (Mon–Fri, 8.30am–5.00pm)	0300 200 3500 0300 200 3519 (Textphone)
Shares & Assets Valuation (Mon–Fri, 8.00am–4.00pm)	0300 123 1082
Stamp Taxes (Mon–Fri, 8.30am–5.00pm)	0300 200 3510
Tax & Benefits Confidential	0300 200 3300

Tax Credits

Helpline:	0345 300 3900 0345 300 3909 (Textphone)
Agent priority line	0345 300 3943
Childcare providers	0345 300 3941

Taxback on Bank and Building Society Interest (Mon–Fri, 8.30am–5.00pm)

	0300 200 3313
Registration Helpline	0300 200 3312

Helplines

Trusts Helpline
(Mon–Fri, 9.00am–5.00am)   0300 123 1072

Welsh language helplines (Mon–Fri, 8.30am–5.00pm)   0300 200 1900 (tax / tax credit)

0300 200 3705 (VAT, customs and excise and duties)

Working Tax Credit/Child Tax Credit Helplines (Mon–Fri, 8.00am–8.00pm; Sat, 8.00am–4.00pm)

Great Britain	0345 300 3900
Northern Ireland	0300 200 3100

Department for Work & Pensions

Benefit Enquiry Line (Mon–Fri, 8.00am–6.00pm)   0800 055 6688

Disability Benefits Helpline   03457 123 456
Textphone for deaf and hard of hearing   0345 7224 433

Class 1A Group (Mon–Fri, 8.00am–5.00pm)   0300 200 3500

Class 2 NIC Helpline (Mon–Fri, 8.30am–5.00pm)   0300 200 3500

Contracted-Out Pensions Helpline (Mon–Fri, 8.00am–5.00pm)   0300 200 3500
0300 200 3519 (Textphone)

NI enquiries for individuals   0300 200 3500
0300 200 3519 (Textphone)

NI Registrations Helpline (Mon–Fri, 8.00am–5.00pm)   0345 600 0643

Pension Credit (Mon–Fri, 8.00am–6.00pm)
Application line   0800 991 234
Textphone for deaf and hard of hearing   0800 169 0133

HMRC – Customs

Customs Confidential (Mon–Sun, 24 hours)   0800 595 000

Customs National Duty Repayment Centre   0300 058 2687

Employer's Helpline	0300 200 3200
(including basic VAT Registration: (Mon–Fri, 8.00am–8.00pm; Sat, 8.00am–4.00pm, closed Sundays, Christmas Day, Boxing Day and New Year's Day)	
National Advice Service Helpline (Mon–Fri, 8.00am–6.00pm)	0300 200 3700
Welsh language users (Mon–Fri, 8.00am–6.00pm)	0300 200 3705
Textphone Service (Mon–Fri, 8.00am–8.00pm)	0300 200 3719
National Insolvency Helpdesk	0300 678 0015

Other useful helplines

Business Support Helpline (Mon–Fri, 9.00am–6.00pm)	0300 456 3565
Business Gateway (Scotland) (Mon–Fri, 8.00am–6pm)	0845 609 6611
Business Wales Helpline (Mon–Fri, 8.30am–5.30pm)	0300 060 3000
Invest Northern Ireland (Mon–Fri, 8.00am–5.00pm)	0800 181 4422
Financial Ombudsman	0800 023 4567 or 0300 123 9 123
(Mon–Fri, 8.00am–8.00pm/Sat 9.00am–1.00pm) The 0300 number is free for mobile phone users who pay a monthly charge for calls to numbers starting 01 or 02.	
National Savings	0500 007 007
Pensions Ombudsman	0207 630 2200
Pension Protection Fund	0345 600 2541
Pensions Regulatory Helpdesk (Mon–Fri, 8.00am–6.00pm)	0345 600 0707
The Pensions Advisory Service (TPAS)	0300 123 1047 (general pensions)

Helplines

(Mon–Fri, 9.00am–5.00pm)

0345 600 0806
(helpline for
women)

0345 602 7021
(helpline for
self-employed)

Useful Internet Sites

HM Revenue & Customs

Forms, leaflets and booklets	www.gov.uk/government/collections/hm-revenue-and-customs-leaflets-factsheets-and-booklets
NIC Information	www.hmrc.gov.uk/ni/index.htm

Government

Department for Business, Innovation and Skills	www.bis.gov.uk
Business Link	www.gov.uk/browse/business
Euro Information	www.gov.uk
Government Gateway	www.gateway.gov.uk
HM Government UK Online	www.gov.uk
HM Treasury	www.hm-treasury.gov.uk
United Kingdom Parliament	www.parliament.uk
UK employment rights	www.gov.uk/browse/working

Regulatory

Financial Reporting Council	www.frc.org.uk
Financial Conduct Authority	www.fca.org.uk
Institute of Chartered Accountants in England & Wales	www.icaew.com
The Association of Chartered Certified Accountants	www.accaglobal.com
Institute of Chartered Accountants of Scotland	www.icas.org.uk

News providers

BBC	www.bbc.co.uk
Tolley	www.tolley.co.uk
LexisNexis	www.lexisnexis.co.uk
Financial Times	www.ft.com
The Guardian	www.guardian.co.uk

Others

Charity Commission for England & Wales	www.charity-commission.gov.uk
The Enhanced Capital Allowance Scheme	www.eca.gov.uk
Europa: The European Union Online	www.europa.eu
Society of Motor Manufacturers and Traders (for CO_2 emission information)	http://www.smmt.co.uk
Vehicle Certification Agency (for CO_2 emission information)	www.dft.gov.uk/vca

General information

Royal Mail (Postcode and address finder service)	www.royalmail.com
National rail enquiries	www.nationalrail.co.uk
UK Street Map	www.streetmap.co.uk